HOW TO BUILD A FERRO-CEMENT BOAT

How to Build a FERRO-CEMENT BOAT

John Samson   Geoff Wellens

SAMSON MARINE DESIGN ENTERPRISES LTD.

INTRODUCTION

THIS book wasn't planned. It just happened. But then, that is not surprising—everything connected with the development of ferro-cement boats, it seems, just happens.

Our own first 'happening' occurred just a few years back when co-author John Samson arrived in Canada to build his first cement boat. John had studied the building techniques in New Zealand for quite some time and was a little surprised to discover that ferro-cement boat-building was a virtually unknown art in North America. He was more than surprised at the developments which followed his initial construction of a Hereshoff 28-foot sailboat.

Among the first things to happen was a fantastic public response to his pioneer effort. People wrote, phoned, and knocked on his door at all hours. They all wanted to know more about ferro-cement boats. More than that, they wanted to build ferro-cement boats themselves. They wanted knowledge which it seemed no one else could supply.

John decided he would try to help. Over a period of time he formed a small company, engaged naval architects and went into the business of supplying plans and building information for ferro-cement boats.

Articles began to appear in magazines and newspapers around the world about the developments in this 'new' boat-building field — and the enquiries poured in from all corners of the globe. For John,

there was a new surprise every day as he carried out more and more research into the building techniques, and, at the same time, kept a hungry boat-building public happy.

It wasn't really surprising that after a couple of years he had gathered so much information that the only way to make it publicly known was to write a book. As John said at the time: "It's all here; it just needs putting together."

And so, this book happened.

The new reader who has not heard of cement boats until picking up this book may well wonder why there was such a staggering response to these early efforts.

There is only one answer—economy.

A boat has been described as a hole in the water into which the owner continually pours money. It is our contention that a ferro-cement boat, which can be built by any careful handyman in his backyard, is the cheapest floating hole available.

The ferro-cement boat, as we will try to explain in the following pages, is writing a revolutionary chapter in the fantastic history of sailing-craft. It is a comparatively new and simple method of boat-construction which brings cruising and everyday sailing within the reach of the average man. It is making staggering inroads into the field of commercial vessels.

No longer must you be a wealthy industrialist to own a 45-foot cruising yacht and sail to the four corners of the world. Ferro-cement is the answer.

Some time ago, John Samson said that he felt in the area of cruising and commercial workboats, ferro-cement would have a greater impact than did the advent of fiberglass in the small boat field. That prediction is already being borne out.

In this book, we have attempted to explain in everyday language how the average man can set about building his dream boat, whether it be a yacht, cruiser or solid work-boat. There are pictures covering the efforts of some pioneer builders—pictures which show more clearly than any words could describe, just what the builder is striving to achieve.

There is a wealth of technical information which may have a limited appeal. But we felt it necessary. To the professional builder or naval architect who wants to work in this new medium, it is essential. And we are fully aware that this is the first handbook and guide ever published on this subject. We have tried to cover the whole subject as fully as possible.

Throughout the preparation of this book we have had the fullest co-operation of the Portland Cement Association. This world-wide organization has made available a wealth of information on the subject of cement and aggregates, and we have received invaluable advice from the Association's scientists, engineers and experts.

Included in the book are a number of excerpts from the Association's own publications, covering the history of cement itself which we found fascinating. We hope the reader will share the interest. We are aware that this bears little connection with the actual construction of a boat but it does help to give one a feeling for the medium.

We have also had great co-operation from naval architects who have been quick to see the value of this new development. The chapter on design speaks for itself—in particular, the designs of Cecil F. Norris, who was the first in North America to meet the challenge of the new medium and capture its excitement in his drawings.

The technical building information and step by step instructions are, of course, culled from the vast experience of John Samson who is certainly a top authority in the field. In addition to his knowledge in this area, John has also been able to call on his wide experience as a top-class boatbuilder and as a seasoned sailor.

This, then, is our sincere attempt to fill what we consider is a definite need. We hope the information on the following pages will help make many people happy boat-owners without the strain of a heavy and continual financial outlay. The ferro-cement boat points the way to the full joy of life afloat.

JOHN SAMSON
GEOFF WELLENS
Vancouver, 1968

CONTENTS

The Ferro-Cement Boat 9

The Old and the New 13

Design: A Thing of Beauty 19

How It All Began 25

A Look at Cement 27

A Look at Wood 39

Reinforcing Bar 45

Some Facts About Wire 47

How to Build the Boat 51

The Cedar Mold Method 71

Miscellaneous Tips 85

Detail Drawings 90

Questions and Answers 98

Design Section 101

The 42-foot salmon troller "Lady Silica", the first North American fishing boat built in ferro-cement.

For the sport fisherman — "Yellow Fin". This ferro-cement 36-footer was built and used for charter work in New Zealand. Below: The graceful 38-foot "Swanhilde" owned and built by Bernie Skinner is pictured here leaving Auckland on the first leg of a world cruise.

CHAPTER 1

THE FERRO-CEMENT BOAT

"A ferro-cement boat. What's that? It'll sink."

That is almost certainly the reaction you will receive if you announce to an unsuspecting world you are about to join the ranks of concrete boat-builders. It's a reaction we have been meeting now for years and one very good reason why this book has been written.

We hope that after reading through the following pages you will have been persuaded to give ferro-cement boats a fair trial and, if you are genuinely interested in building or owning a boat, will agree with us that this construction method opens the door to sailing for thousands of people.

But, first of all, back to that question, "What is a ferro-cement boat?"

Very briefly, you can answer the question by saying it is a boat built basically from such inexpensive materials as chicken wire, water piping, common steel bars and, of course, cement. The average construction methods are simple and for a very low initial outlay you produce a boat which is fantastically strong —it's actually gaining strength throughout it's life— a boat which is fireproof, virtually maintenance free, and thoroughly seaworthy.

If anyone persists in the argument that it will sink— obviously through a preconceived relation of cement to stone—the simplest answer is to point to the many boats built from steel. And, if that fails, it is also worth mentioning that wooden boats more often than not weigh many tons, with heavy ballast and machinery installed.

It's all a matter of acceptance—and ferro-cement boats have been fighting for quite some time to break down a barrier of prejudice.

You might ask why, if the boats are as good as we have already stated, they are not in common usage. Let's face it. Ferro-cement boats are not new and have been around for over 100 years.

Probably the biggest single reason why this acceptance is slow is that the ferro-cement boat's 20th century predecessors left behind a bad image. Yes, we mean the cement boat of the war years, and the cement boats of pre-war years which now lie crumbling in various ports around the world.

There is a tremendous difference between those crumbling hulks of patchwork masonry and the ferro-cement boat of today. The construction concept is totally different and it would be quite unfair to try and draw a comparison in the finished product.

But, unfortunately, whenever the ferro-cement boat is mentioned, the image it projects is that of the old crumbling hulk. This handbook is written in a bid to break down that image and put this relatively new and extremely exciting method of construction into proper perspective.

The cement boats which we will be talking about and describing in these pages are all new and exciting

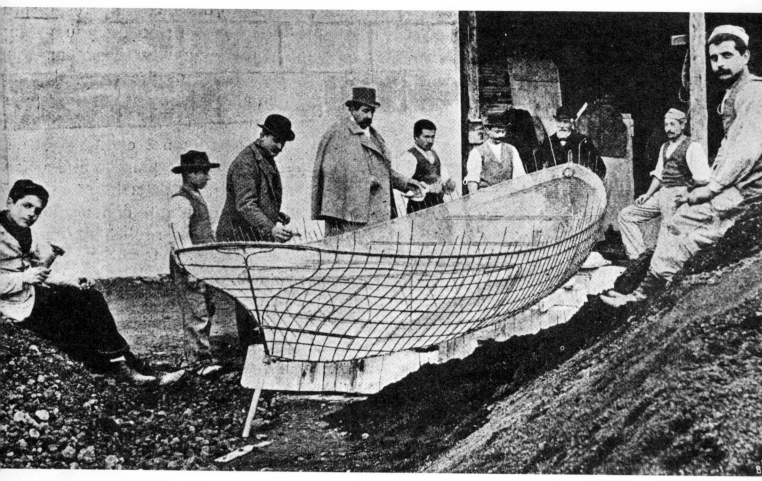

The date is 1896, the place is Rome. The boat is the handiwork of Carlos Gabellini.

Built in Great Britain in 1919 the cement S.S. Armistice undergoes sea trials.

boats which will prove their worth time and again, whether in pleasure or commercial fields, boats which the sailor can be proud to own.

The earliest recorded evidence of ferro-cement boat construction credits the Frenchman, Jean Louis Lambot as the "inventor". Using a mesh impregnated with mortar, Lambot built his first small boat in 1848. This boat, in remarkably good condition, can still be seen at the Brignoles museum.

Lambot went on to build a second boat in 1849 and this has been displayed in a Paris museum which has now closed down.

Other boat builders followed Lambot's lead and a concrete scow, built in 1887, is still in regular use at the Amsterdam Zoo.

The Italian, Carlos Gabellini, was another early "ferro-cement" builder but, for the present-day development and refinement of the medium the credit goes to another Italian. He is Professor Luigi Nervi of the firm Nervi & Bertoli.

Widely, if somewhat mistakenly, regarded as the "founder" of ferro-cement, Nervi began his work in the field in the early 1940's.

He began by looking back to the years between 1917 and 1922, when approximately 150,000 tons of shipping were produced in cement—these crumbling hulks to which we have previously referred. But, of course, at that time, the development of reinforced concrete was in its infancy and many aspects were not understood.

Main faults were the excessive corrosion factor of the reinforcing materials and the inefficient weight factor. As we said, all around the world today you can find examples of these ships, barges and pontoons. Some, perhaps surprisingly, are still in relatively good condition and in the next section of the book, we will take a look at one such example, in Powell River, Canada.

But back to Nervi.

By the 1930's, engineers had overcome most of the technical problems presented by reinforced concrete but they were still coming up with a mixture which was far too thick and heavy for commercial use—particularly in the shipping field.

Appreciating these problems, Nervi in 1943 began his experiments using many layers of fine wire mesh impregnated with the cement mortar. The results were startling.

At the time he said: "The material created did not behave like regular concrete but presented all the mechanical characteristics of a homogenous material. Experiments proved it would withstand great strains without formation of cracks in the cement mortar as a result of subdivision of the reinforcement.

"Impact tests in which a weight of 580 pounds was dropped from heights of up to ten feet showed this very high strength in a slab only 1.1 inch thick. These tests showed, moreover, that even when a slab failed, the weight did not break through them. Even when the cement cracked extensively and the steel yielded, the slab did not disintegrate and they still prevented water seeping through in great quantities."

The ferro-cement boat was on its way.

Soon after the war, Nervi and Bertoli built their first vessel, the 165-ton motor-sailer, *Irene*. The craft proved beyond doubt the simplicity of the construction procedure and a perfect correlation between actual and predicted behaviour.

The construction of *Irene* required no forms. The total weight of the hull came out at five percent less than the weight of a comparative wooden hull and, most important, it cost some 40 percent less.

This hull proved perfectly tight in the water and from the inside the part above the water line could not be distinguished from below because there were absolutely no moist patches. After years of hard service in the Mediterranean the hull was, and still is, as new as the day it was built and has never required any maintenance.

Many, many refinements were yet to be made in the art of ferro-cement boat construction, but Professor Nervi had kindled the flame.

Design technique in particular was to see rapid improvement and a later section of this book covers this topic more fully (see page 19).

Among the first to adopt the new building method were the ever-eager New Zealand yachtsmen. And experiments quickly followed in England, Canada and North America.

In this summary of the ferro-cement boat and its development, it is now perhaps time to take a closer look at the advantages which the medium offers. As we said, you are building a boat from low-cost materials which include common-or-garden water piping, chicken wire, perhaps a little timber (cedar preferably) and cement. As a general guide you will be striving to construct a hull which will have a thickness of no more than three-quarters of an inch, but which will possess the strength of steel. And that hull is impervious to corrosion, rotting or the teredo worm. Nor is it damaged by the ultra-violet rays of the sun and, as a one-piece construction, neither does it suffer from leaky fastenings or joints. Electrolysis and galvanic action is minimal.

There are basically two methods of construction and these are discussed at length in a later section (see page 51). For the moment, it is sufficient to say that either method can be tackled with confidence by the amateur.

Nothing, of course, is perfect and the ferro-cement boat does have its faults. Or, in particular, one big fault. This is the limitation of boat size to which the medium can be applied.

Naval architects are now taking further steps in design and it will not be long before plans will be available for boats in the 20 to 120-foot range. At present, however, few designs are available outside a 30 to 60-foot range.

All the designs reproduced in this book are from the drawing boards of the Samson Marine Design Enterprise Company in Canada and represent the fullest range available. They are among the first drawn specifically for the ferro-cement medium.

Many of the earlier experiments involved the use of plans for wooden boats. The design section of this book points to the dangers inherent in this practice and perhaps points to another reason why development of the ferro-cement boat has been so slow. Until recent years, no plans were available for the medium.

Using the plans now available, however, the do-it-yourself builder or the commercial sailor who will employ a professional to build his boat, will find distinctive cost advantages. The price of wire mesh, piping and cement is amazingly low when compared to timber or steel. For example, a 30-foot hull should not cost any more than $900 for materials.

The final plastering of the boat or the cementing, does require special attention. The finish of the boat depends entirely on the success of this one-shot operation and it is always advisable in this area to have a professional man on hand.

And, while we are discussing the expected cost of a ferro-cement boat it should be remembered that the price of the bare hull is only a portion of the finished cost of any boat. Ferro-cement will only offer a saving in that regard.

It is time now, however, to forget the theorizing and to look at the bare facts.

And before we set about telling you how to build your ferro-cement boat, let us look at an example of the old crumbling hulks and then on to what is probably the most successful ferro-cement boat sailing today, the 53-foot cutter *Awahnee,* owned by globetrotter Dr. Bob Griffith of California.

Built in 1887 and still happily afloat. This Dutch boat was pictured on a pond at Amsterdam Zoo in 1967 by B. J. deRuiter.

And even further into the past. Lambot's original boat built in 1848 now rests in the Brignoles Museum, France.

CHAPTER 2

THE OLD AND THE NEW

One of the most amazing examples of the durability of cement and yet, at the same time, a distressing example of the misuse of the medium in the shipping field, exists at Powell River, British Columbia, Canada.

There ten ships, or ten floating hulks, have been chained together to form a floating breakwater for log booms. It is known as the Powell River Mill Log Pond breakwater — a floating monument to unknown pioneers of the medium.

Nine of the ships are of concrete and one of steel. The ship lengths vary from 230-feet for the steel hulk to 420-feet for the largest concrete hulk, the *Peralta.* The majority of the concrete hulks are in the 350-foot range.

The floating breakwater was started many years ago using floating booms, Davis rafts, floating timber cribs, wooden ships, steel ships and finally concrete ships.

The concrete hulks were first purchased by the MacMillan, Bloedel and Powell River Co. in 1947 and 1948 and were found to give the longest service life. In fact, the hulks installed in 1947 are in perfectly good condition today, probably due to the fact that concrete, unlike other building materials, gets stronger as it gets older.

At one time there were two ex-U.S. steel warships in the breakwater as well as a steel oil tanker. One warship, the *Huron,* sank in 1960 and presently lies at the bottom beneath one of the concrete hulks.

The concrete hulks were all built during the war years. Some were used as freighters, some oil and gasoline barges, and the *Peralta,* built as far back as 1916, was a floating sardine factory for much of her career in Alaska.

Tonnage of these vessels ranges from approximately 2,000 capacity to 10,000 capacity while the dead weight of the ships varies between 800 and 5,000 tons.

At present, the hulks are ballasted, some with gravel and others with water. This is to lower the hulks into the water at depths of up to 15 feet to break severe wave action.

The ships were all built in the U.S., except, that is, for the steel sister of the line—a product of a Scottish shipyard.

All ships in the breakwater are anchored using 14 and 16 ton anchors with eight to ten anchors per vessel. The hulks are in water which ranges in depth from 5 to 200 feet and each ship is connected to the other with bridle chains.

During storms the ships have been known to drag their anchors shoreward showing the tremendous forces at work and, every five or ten years, the breakwater has to be repositioned. Also, quite regularly, the anchor chains which corrode away, usually at the ocean floor, have to be replaced. This work is tackled

by skin-divers and on one repair job, the divers had to remove a 12-foot octopus from the corroded chain before it could be replaced.

The reason for the floating breakwater at Powell River is that the mill site, harbour and log pond are exposed to severe south easterly and north westerly winds. A rock breakwater would have cost millions of dollars in the deep water. The floating breakwater of concrete hulks has cost only a fraction of that figure.

As we said, a floating monument to cement but hardly a shrine at which ferro-cement designers and builders would wish to worship.

One shrine to which ferro-cement builders turn however, if not Nervi's *Irene,* is the *Awahnee,* the 53-foot cutter built in 1963 by California veterinarian, Dr. Bob Griffith. The success of this boat, built in New Zealand by Dr. Griffith to his own design and modifications, has spread to all corners of the world. But then, Dr. Griffith has sailed *Awahnee* to all corners of the world and is still seeking out the nooks and crannies he has missed.

In 1967 Dr. Griffith estimated he had travelled some 150,000 ocean miles and twice circumnavigated the globe. The first circumnavigation was in the original wooden *Awahnee* and the second in the ferro-cement version.

Dr. Griffith is, today, one of the foremost authorities on ferro-cement construction and, understandably, an expert on its behaviour under field-testing conditions. In fact, his own book on ferro-cement boats and his travels will prove a valuable addition to the printed material available on the subject.

In 1967 the co-author of this handbook, as boating editor of the Vancouver *Daily Province,* had the good fortune to interview Dr. Griffith and spend some time aboard *Awahnee.* At that time, the Griffiths were sailing the ferro-cement cutter from Alaska after visiting Japan and sailing up through the Aleutian Islands.

The two articles are reprinted here in part to show the value of a ferro-cement sailing vessel and, in part, the joy of blue water cruising. In this way, too, we pay tribute to Dr. Bob Griffith, a true pioneer of ferro-cement boats.

Now just part of a breakwater, the concrete ship "Quartz".

The combined talents of Hollywood's finest could never have produced the factual story of Dr. Griffith and his eight years of ocean cruising aboard the 53-foot *Awahnee.*

Yet the story of the California veterinarian who forsook his practice and cattle ranch for a life at sea actually began on Hollywood's doorstep.

The adventures which have befallen Dr. Griffith with over 150,000 miles of ocean, have that touch of the unbelievable that only the truth can fashion. Two complete circumnavigations of the globe, twice shipwrecked, a 138-knot windstorm off Gibraltar, twice arrested—once on suspicion of being an atomic spy, once suspected of gun-running. These are but a few of the many adventures.

The story starts in California in 1959 where Dr. Griffith began his search for the boat to carry him to his adventures at sea.

He found his original *Awahnee,* a spartan but seaworthy cutter, built by an Englishman and his family, in the bay area of San Francisco.

After a shakedown cruise up and down the California coast, Dr. Griffith set off on his first real trip —carrying a scientific exploration party to the Marquesas. More charter trips followed, forward and back across the Pacific as Dr. Griffith fully tested *Awahnee.* She was a thoroughbred in every detail. Soon he reached farther, sailing to New Zealand where he planned to settle for a while. After a couple of months ashore he couldn't stand it any longer and *Awahnee* was off again—this time heading west on the first circum-navigation bid.

It was plain sailing until *Awahnee,* with her crew of five, reached the Red Sea. There came the first disaster.

Miles from shore, the cutter impaled herself on an uncharted reef. Holed in seven places, she lodged firmly on the razorsharp coral and, try as he might, Dr. Griffith couldn't float her free. It was obvious he would have to go ashore to try to summon aid.

"But," as Dr. Griffith ruefully says, "that was much easier said than done. No fewer than 250 ships passed by us as we flew our distress signals but they all ignored us. We sat there for four days before a vessel eventually came over and, after much haggling, took me off.

"Of course, politics were involved here and I could get no help, so I decided after 11 days to go back and float *Awahnee* free myself. I did it with dynamite—literally blowing her off the reef and then heading for shore as fast as I could."

Said Dr. Griffith with a smile: "That was quite something, I can tell you. There's something strange about steering a keeler which is half full of water. Particularly when it is night and you are in a main shipping channel with no lights. However, we beached safely and later made Port Tewfik where we completed repairs."

The sea miles were slipping behind *Awahnee* now, the months were turning into years. It was into the Mediterranean next for more weeks and months of idyllic cruising but, another adventure was close at hand. That was when Dr. Griffith headed for the Gibraltar Straits and the open Atlantic.

"We had already experienced quite a bit of bad weather and considered ourselves quite competent to stand the worst storms. But we hadn't counted on what hit us there. We were later told that the official weather station had recorded winds of up to 138 knots. We weren't far from land and eventually made a safe anchorage—but, boy, did we take a battering in that! You just wouldn't believe the seas that were running."

Awahnee next made her maiden crossing of the Atlantic. "We did it in just over 11 days," recalls Dr. Griffith. "It was perfect sailing."

Through the Panama to the west coast—and the first circumnavigation was completed.

But time was running short for the wooden-planked original *Awahnee*.

After a few more months of happy cruising and racing, the doctor at sea began a search of uncharted islands in the South Pacific for an American yacht which was reported missing. First he had to clear his name after being accused by French authorities of gun-running. "It was a completely false charge but it took me quite a time to clear up the mess," he says.

Then the search. "There was good reason to believe the crew had survived and were living on one of the countless uncharted islands. In the search I found three other unreported shipwrecks—but not the one I searched for."

And, from that search *Awahnee* herself never returned.

"We had now been at sea for almost four years and our search for the missing American yacht in the uncharted islands of the South Pacific was proving fruitless."

And, added Dr. Griffith as he recounted his adventures spanning eight years at sea and covering 150,000 ocean miles, "I now believe that no matter how good a sailor you are, some day you will inevitably lose your boat. It is just a matter of time. I wasn't thinking of that, however, as we completed the search which had lasted for two months. And, in retrospect, I know I made the mistake that cost me the original *Awahnee*.

"We were sheltering off the lee of an island and I was completely fooled by the fact that it was circular. I thought we were safe, yet all the time we were being carried by the current toward a reef.

Dr. Bob Griffith and family sail against the Honolulu skyline in their 53-foot ferro-cement cutter "Awahnee".

"When we struck, the *Awahnee* foundered almost immediately. Her keel came away with a sickening noise and immediately she started to break up. We got away with as much as we could to the island, then began the week-long back-breaking task of stripping off and salvaging as much of value as we could. We took off masts, winches, sails, rigging—in fact everything of any redeemable value. But by the end of the week *Awahnee* was gone. Not one piece of wood more than two feet in length was left of her. It was a sad moment—but we also had our problems.

"As far as we knew the island was uninhabited and uncharted. However, after five days, we discovered two native Tahitians on the island gathering copra. One of them, Teka, is now in my crew. We eventually got word to the French authorities of our plight when the copra trading schooner called at the island. However, we were there for 67 days in all. It was a wonderful experience."

The "rescue" of the *Awahnee* crew from the island provides, however, one of the highlights of Dr. Griffith's adventures.

"Eventually the French sent their gendarmes to pick us up. The scene is as vivid in my mind today as it was then. The gendarme strode through the surf up to the beach to meet me. I was standing in tattered underwear and a cap, all the clothing I had left. He extended his hand and said 'Dr. Griffith, I presume!' It was unbelievable—but not more unbelievable than what happened next. We were all taken to Tahiti and put under guard. We were regarded as dangerous atomic spies!"

Adds Dr. Griffith: "It took some time to sort that problem out and I can tell you the French authorities got a few rude blasts from me before it was all over."

But finally, Dr. Griffith was allowed to leave. He bought another boat and immediately set sail for New Zealand where he planned to build another *Awahnee* —but this time of cement.

"I had heard and seen something of this new building technique and figured if it was as good as everyone claimed, it was the answer for me. I have now proved, of course, that it was the answer. But before we began to build the new *Awahnee* I travelled all over New Zealand to see every concrete boat that was being built. There were good ones and bad ones. One was so bad the builder eventually bulldozed a hole and just buried it.

"We made slight modifications in design from the original but just five and one-half months later we were ready to sail off again."

The new ferro-cement *Awahnee* which sailed out to begin the second circumnavigation of the globe by Dr. Griffith was the first concrete boat to undergo any severe sea test.

"I didn't know what to expect from the boat at the time," recalled Dr. Griffith. "She looked great and had actually come out a couple of tons lighter than the wooden original. We soon got our first test, however. Just three days out we were caught in a storm with winds up to 70 knots and the new *Awahnee* came through with flying colors. Our confidence in the ferrocement boat was bolstered at once and we have never looked back."

On this trip, the crossing of the Indian Ocean provided the first real adventure. That was when Dr. Griffith's wife Nancy was thrown overboard into the shark-infested waters.

Says Dr. Griffith: "We had good following winds and I was driving under twin headsails. I decided I would experiment with the mainsail up, as well, and Nancy was kneeling on a fold in the sail while I took the halyard. Suddenly a gust of wind caught the canvas and the sail ballooned out in one great rush. Nancy was literally catapulted over the side—clearing the safety lines by at least six feet. We swung around and headed back after throwing out every piece of floating life-gear available. With the winds strengthening it was no easy job and when we did reach the flotation gear there was no sign of Nancy.

"It took me a few seconds to realize that this gear had also been blown along by the winds and I looked farther back for any sign of her. Luckily I spotted her waving and yelling on the crest of a wave.

"We made two unsuccessful downwind passes before we managed to get her on board. Ever since then, I have recommended that any floating life-saving gear should be attached to a sea anchor."

On went *Awahnee* to South Africa, rounding the Cape of Good Hope and then heading out again across the South Atlantic.

"I hadn't decided at that time to try to round the Horn," recalls Dr. Griffith. "It was only when we reached South America that I took that decision. As it turned out it was pretty uneventful. In fact I enjoyed it immensely.

"There are countless good anchorages there and we simply did what the old clipper ships and schooners used to do. We would lie off in the lee of an island waiting for a good spell of weather and then take off through the outer passage. The country around there is fantastic with good hunting and fishing. I would like to go back and sail round in a dinghy just for the hell of it."

The second circumnavigation was drawing to a close. *Awahnee* was back in her South Pacific home. After more cruising, Dr. Griffith headed for Japan where in recent months he completed his first full-length book on his travels.

From Japan he sailed up through the Aleutians to Alaska and finally down to Vancouver where he met up with his former cruising compatriot and fellow cement boat builder, John Samson, pioneer of the new building technique in Canada.

Looking back over his eight years at sea, Dr. Griffith says, "I wouldn't exchange it for anything. And there are still so many places that we have yet to visit and revisit. The thought of settling down just frightens me."

Perhaps he has been frightened by his experience of traffic some years back. That was when he stopped in San Francisco, hired a car and went straight out onto the rush - hour freeway where the cars were bumper to bumper at 60 miles an hour. "That was terrifying," he recalls. "I had come across nothing like it in all my time at sea."

And in those eight years, Dr. Griffith has had no fewer than 150 people sail with him. "Of all those," he says, "only three would not be invited back again."

When he visited Vancouver he had on board *Awahnee* his wife and 13-year old son, Reid, not to mention Teka, the Tahitian whom he met gathering copra on the uncharted South Sea island, and Californian Justine Black.

"In the future," Dr. Griffith says, "I want to show people just how good the ferro-cement boat is and I just want to sail off and see all the places we have missed so far."

It seems another 150,000 sea miles and at least eight years of adventure lie ahead of Dr. Bob Griffith, sailor of fortune, and his ferro-cement *Awahnee*.

There, then, you have cement boats—the old and the new. From the breakwater hulks of Powell River to the sleek and beautiful lines of *Awahnee*. A rapid jump in technique and knowledge and what lies ahead?

Let us now look at the question of ferro-cement boat design and how it is approached by the naval architect.

The oceans of the world have slipped swiftly beneath "Awahnee's" keel.

CHAPTER 3

DESIGN — A THING OF BEAUTY

Any boat, no matter what material she is constructed from, must have beauty. Whether it be the shape of her transom, the lines of her sheer or just her overall appeal, the boat *must* have visual attraction.

At the same time, the designer will tell you she must be practical, seaworthy and seakindly. After all, even if she looks good but doesn't sail worth a damn, she's no use.

This is the philosophy of naval architect Cecil F. Norris, chief designer of the Samson Marine Design Enterprise Company, and one of the first to apply the eye-appeal yardstick to this medium.

Norris always works on the principle that as much art as science should be applied to any design and that overall, any design is a matter of compromise.

When he first looked at the problems presented by ferro-cement design, Norris was quick to see that basically the boat would be of heavy displacement. While this would be considered a disadvantage by some people, it contributes to seakindliness and comfort.

And, of course, there were other advantages such as low cost and having a relatively simple medium with which to work. Aluminum for example is not only expensive, but also proves a difficult working material. This is particularly so when you introduce the field to the amateur builder.

The steel boat had nothing to offer that was more advantageous than ferro-cement. Again, it was difficult to construct and expensive and, of course, suffered extensively from corrosion and galvanic action.

The wooden boat, he argued, was also more expensive and, while probably more flexible in the size ratios, proved a difficult and time-consuming medium.

Looking at the roominess factor, Norris immediately saw that because the ferro-cement hull basically required no interior frames, tremendous possibilities opened up. A 36-foot design in ferro-cement would have far more to offer than its conventional cousin.

Skin-thickness and frame space would account for a tremendous space volume. While the average ferro-cement boat had a hull thickness of three-quarters of an inch, a comparable wooden boat would have a planking of at least 1½ inches and in many cases 2 inches—with frames, a total of 4 inches. The volume that this difference represents in available internal space can only be described as staggering. It can perhaps be appreciated best if you visualize a circle with a 9-foot diameter. Another circle of 12-foot diameter has double the volume!

Apply that rule to the 36-foot boat and you can see Norris's argument. And, what is more important, to compensate for the weight factor, the architect realized he would have to increase the boat's beam. This gave him even more inside room.

The value of this becomes still more apparent when

you look closer at cost comparisons of the differing mediums.

An aluminum 40-footer will cost at least four or five times as much as the ferro-cement craft. In steel the cost would be more than doubled. Ferro-cement would be not more than half the cost of wood.

And, of course, for that you are also getting much more boat!

Norris next looked at the weight factor and decided on compromise. Because of weight and the fact that she would be a heavy displacement boat, she had to be wider.

In a conventional boat of wooden construction, permanent ballast runs anywhere between 25 per cent and 75 per cent of the total weight of the finished craft. In cement, he figured, it shouldn't be more than 25 per cent.

The answer then was to apply geometry. Increase the width while retaining draft, thus giving the boat good stability without sacrificing performance.

This, of course, introduced another compromise. Application of geometry to improve stability produced a greater wetted surface area, and this relates to sail area.

Normal sail area is 2¼ to 2½ times the wetted surface area. Norris had to increase his sail area accordingly.

So he had to come up with the ideal, which was a vessel built of ferro-cement that had the least possible displacement, the least wetted surface area, the greatest stability and the correct amount of sail area to make her perform well. And, of course, she had to be beautiful.

These factors he applied to the 45-foot ketch *C-Breeze* which is among the designs included in this book.

This particular design also involved the introduction of a lengthy keel, partly because of the essentials required by the compromise and partly because this boat was primarily designed for charter work. With her extreme roominess she was, of course, a natural for the latter type of duty.

Norris figured if she was to spend long times out at sea, possibly riding out rough weather, the lengthy keel would enable her to stand hove to for days on end and maintain her position.

And, of course, the long straight keel improved headroom throughout the boat.

Ferro-cement boats can be and have been designed with moderate length keels. Here another rule applies. The lateral area of a boat, that is the silhouette of the underwater portion, should be about one-seventh the sail area. So it's back to the old compromise of wetted surface area, displacement, and sail area. One factor depends on the other and the hallmark of any good design is excellent use of that compromise.

In brief, the considerable displacement inherent in a ferro-cement boat means considerable wetted surface. This in turn gives considerable sail area, calling for considerable silhouette area. A vicious circle if you like.

And that probably answers the many enquiries for a shallow-draft ferro-cement design. As yet it is difficult to achieve, but not impossible.

Norris himself says this is best achieved by the use of a centre-board and the first designs incorporating this feature have now been produced.

With a centre-board the problem to be conquered is leakage—a problem which is far from insurmountable. Fortunately, many products on the market today bond perfectly with the cement. Rubber, plastics, and steel can all be safely buried in cement in the construction stages to form an effective leak-proof entry for a centre-board. Research is now being carried out in this area and no problems are expected.

Turning to other advantages of the medium for the designer, Norris points firmly to the fact that shapes can be built in cement that couldn't even be attempted in wood. There is no need for even one flat surface in a ferro-cement design—and curves give added strength.

The ferro-cement medium also reduces to a minimum that old enemy of the salt water sailor—electrolysis. This is the combination of various metals in seawater which set up a natural battery. In ferro-cement construction, with all metals buried in the mortar, there is no danger.

The commercial fisherman, says Norris, is probably the one who will benefit most from the development of ferro-cement design.

First and foremost the cost factor is in the favour of a man who is using the boat as a means of livelihood. His initial outlay is low. Following this is the fact that his further maintenance costs will be cut to a minimum.

In commercial use, the increase in interior volume gives him greater carrying capacity than his competitor and profit advantages are obvious. Even without the greater volume, his carrying capacity would increase anyway by the mere fact that scantlings or the sizes of materials used in conventional craft are much larger than in ferro-cement.

Ferro-cement, unlike most other boat-building materials, becomes stronger if it is kept wet or damp. Ferro-cement is excellent for fish-holds and brine tanks. Concrete may be buried beneath insulation without any rot or rust problems developing. Once the insulation is applied a tough concrete skin may be applied on top of this. This skin is smooth and can be readily cleaned—an advantage to the fisherman who is handling perishable food. The holds, fuel and water tanks can all be built into the boat as an integral part of the structure.

Nor is there much fear of design standardization in the medium. While fiberglass craft must essentially be all of a sameness through the use of a 'plug' in construction, ferro-cement boats can be one-of-a-kind.

Even if a number of hulls are produced to a similar pattern, any type of above deck finishing can be added.

And the commercial man or the cruising sailor can forget leakage problems. A ferro-cement hull won't leak and no caulking is required.

Then, finally, we come to the area of repair where again Norris stresses a fantastic advantage. That is assuming a ferro-cement boat would ever require a repair job.

Repairs to a ferro-cement hull can almost be carried out on the spot. Experience has shown that the skin has good impact resistance. It would require a tremendous impact with a sharply pointed object to pierce the hull. At most, a collision would produce an egg-shell type fracture. This could be repaired simply in a matter of hours.

Actual proof of the strength and amazing durability has been experienced by both Dr. Bob Griffith and Gordon Ellis, a Canadian builder of commercial fishing vessels.

Dr. Griffith scraped his *Awanhee* along the side of an iceberg during his cruise around Cape Horn. After crossing the Pacific Ocean without checking the vessel he later discovered a slight 8-inch gash in the side of the hull.

Ellis' experience was even more impressive.

He smashed his 42-foot troller onto a submerged reef while out taking publicity pictures with a photographer. He hit the reef while travelling at about 11 knots and literally bounced right over the top of the rock formation. He headed straight for the marine ways to inspect the damage. He found nothing more than a long scrape along the bilge. Unable to believe his eyes, he went back to the area at low tide to see what he had hit and found a huge rock formation completely sheared off—oysters and everything!

Needless to say, Griffith and Ellis have every confidence in the strength of their hulls.

All that remains to be considered, then, is the future of ferro-cement design.

Norris feels that because essentially you can work to any shape you desire in the medium, a whole field of design is untouched. And improvements in the thickness of the medium—or rather the continual striving towards a lighter mixture and thinner skin—will only enlarge the field.

Says Norris: "It is probably very similar to the work in fiberglass design in the early 50's. At first they designed wooden boats in fiberglass just as they did with the ferro-cement a couple of years back."

A boat shape should be designed bearing in mind the materials to be used throughout construction. The weight and strength of these materials are taken into consideration. There are very few materials which fall within a 10 per cent weight range. Consequently, on a 20-ton vessel, over 2 tons difference would be the minimum if a wooden boat were converted to a ferro-cement boat, a fiberglass boat converted to a steel boat, etc. Therefore, it is very important to build a hull of the material the boat was *designed* to be built from. Normally there are many thousands of dollars invested in a finished boat and the cost of plans normally runs between 1 and 3 per cent. Purchasing proper plans is a good investment to ensure the finished boat will perform successfully.

"Now," Norris points out, "the first steps have been taken but the design cannot yet be stretched too far. Some of the possibilities are staggering but at the same time, as yet, unacceptable. But then, many of the things they are now doing with fiberglass, would have been totally unacceptable years ago.

"It is perhaps enough for the moment to get ferro-cement itself accepted as a highly competitive medium. Then we can look ahead and remember that design is as much art as science."

A 36-foot ferro-cement Matangi-class keeler awaits launching day in New Zealand.

Out earning her keep on New Zealand's fishing grounds — the 36-foot "Yellow Fin".

Voyage almost complete. The 53-foot "Awahnee" sits at anchor in Vancouver, Canada, on her winter passage to California.

Smooth sailing for "White Heather", the 41-foot Orams design owned and built by New Zealand's Scotty Jenkins.

The bare hull of the Matangi-class motor-sailer.

The 55-foot "Falcon", owned and built by Brian Walden of Auckland, New Zealand, heads for the starting line of the 1100-mile Suva Race.

CHAPTER 4

HOW IT ALL BEGAN

The story of how cement was first discovered is both fascinating and informative. It has been compiled by experts of the Portland Cement Association and the account is of interest to anyone contemplating construction of a ferro-cement boat.

Ever since man first started to build he sought a material that would turn stones into a solid formed mass. The Assyrians and Babylonians used clay for the purpose and the Egyptians advanced to the discovery of lime and gypsum mortar as a binding agent for building such structures as the Pyramids.

The Greeks made further improvements and finally the Romans developed a cement that produced structures of remarkable durability.

Most of the building foundations in the Roman Forum were constructed of a form of concrete placed in some locations to a depth of 12 feet. The great Roman baths built around 27 B.C., the Colosseum and the Basilica of Constantine are examples of early Roman architecture in which cement mortar was used.

The secret of the Roman success was traced to the mixing of slaked lime with pozzolana, a volcanic ash from Mount Vesuvius. This process produced a cement capable of hardening under water.

During the Middle Ages this art was unfortunately lost and it was not until the scientific spirit of enquiry revived that men rediscovered the secret of hydraulic cement—cement that would harden under water.

Repeated structural failure of the Eddystone Lighthouse off the coast of Cornwall, England, led John Smeaton, a British engineer, to conduct experiments with mortars in fresh and salt water. In 1756 these tests led to the discovery that cement made from limestone containing a considerable proportion of clay would harden under water. Using this finding the Eddystone Lighthouse was rebuilt in 1759 and stood for 126 years before being replaced.

Other men experimenting in the same field during the period from 1756 to 1830 included L. J. Vicat and Lesage in France, and Joseph Parker and James Frost in England.

However, it was not until 1824 that Joseph Aspdin, a bricklayer and mason in Leeds, England, took out a patent on a hydraulic cement which he called portland cement. He took the name from the color of the cement which resembled the stone quarried on the Island of Portland, off the British coast.

Aspdin's method involved the careful proportioning of limestone and clay, pulverizing them, and burning the mixture into clinker which was then ground into the finished cement. Portland cement today, as in Aspdin's day, is a predetermined and carefully proportioned chemical combination of calcium, silicon, iron and aluminum.

The earlier natural cements gave way to the portland cement which is a predictable known product of consistently high quality. Today, about 98 per cent of the cement produced is portland cement.

In Aspdin's day, however, the new product caught on slowly. He established a plant in Wakefield to manufacture the portland cement, some of which was used in the construction of the Thames River Tunnel.

But it was only 20 years later when J. D. White and Sons set up a prosperous factory in Kent, that the new industry saw its greatest expansion. It spread to Belgium and Germany and in 1859-1867, portland cement was used to build the London sewer system.

The first recorded shipment of portland cement reached the United States in 1868 when European manufacturers began shipping the product as ballast in tramp steamers at very low freight rates. The volume increased until 1895 when the Americans began producing their own portland cement.

By then, portland cement production was spreading to other countries around the world. Joseph Aspdin, using his crude method of burning powdered limestone and clay in his kitchen stove, had laid the foundations of an industry which now, annually, processes literally mountains of limestone, clay, and cement rock into a powder so fine it will pass through a sieve capable of holding water. So fine, in fact, that one pound of cement contains 150 billion grains.

That then, in brief, was how it all began.

But now, let us look a little closer at the cement itself, its contents and value in the field of ferrocement construction.

Launching day for a ferro-cement tug-boat. The "Ce-Fer Made" was built by the Ce-Fer Company of Vancouver, Canada.

CHAPTER 5

A LOOK AT CEMENT

In properly made mortar, each particle of aggregate, no matter how large or how small, is completely surrounded by paste and all spaces between aggregate particles are completely filled with paste. The aggregates are considered as inert materials while the paste (cement and water) is the cementing medium which binds the aggregate particles into a solid mass. It can be readily understood, therefore, that the quality of the concrete is greatly dependent on the quality of the paste and that the paste must have the strength, durability and resistance to the passage of water required in boat hulls.

The cementing or binding properties of the paste are due to chemical reactions between the cement and water. These reactions require time and favourable conditions as to temperature and moisture. They take place very rapidly at first and then more slowly for a long time under favourable conditions. Although a relatively small amount of water is required to complete the chemical reactions, more water is used for the sake of placing the mortar. As the paste is thinned out with water, however, its quality is lowered; it has less strength and becomes less resistant to the elements. For successful results, then, a proper proportion of water to cement is essential.

The paste ordinarily constitutes 50 per cent of the total volume of mortar. The absolute volume of cement is usually 30 per cent and the water approximately 20 per cent. Thus something like 50 per cent of the mortar is made up of the aggregates. Since the aggregates constitute such a large part of the mortar, care in their selection is important. They should be graded to secure the optimum strength with the paste, and they must be made up of particles having ample strength and resistance to exposure conditions. They must not contain materials having injurious effects. In the following discussion it is assumed that suitable aggregates are used.

Impermeable Mortar:

On boat work it is important that the mortar be watertight. Imperviousness is an essential requirement of mortar exposed to salt water or other severe conditions. This requires a watertight or impermeable paste. Tests show that the permeability or watertightness of the paste is dependent on the amount of mixing water used and the extent to which the chemical reactions between the cement and water have progressed.

Moist Curing:

The increase in strength with age is true so long as drying of the mortar is prevented. When the mortar is permitted to dry, the chemical reactions cease. It is, therefore, desirable to keep the mortar moist as long as possible. These statements are illustrated on Page

36 where it is shown that concrete kept constantly moist has much higher strength than concrete allowed to dry. It also shows that when moist curing is discontinued, the strength increases for a short period and then does not increase further to any extent.

Effect of Temperature:

The temperature at which mortar is made and cured affects the rate at which the reactions between cement and water progress. On this page curves are shown for concrete mixed, placed and cured at temperatures of 40 to 120 degrees F. All ingredients were at mixing temperature when mixing started. It is seen that at a temperature above normal, 73 degrees, the strengths are higher the first few days but lower at later periods. At 55 degrees, concrete had lower strengths than normal for the first 10 days or so but then had slightly higher strengths than normal. Concrete made and cured at 40 degrees had lower strengths than normal at all ages. At temperatures below freezing there is a very little increase in strength.

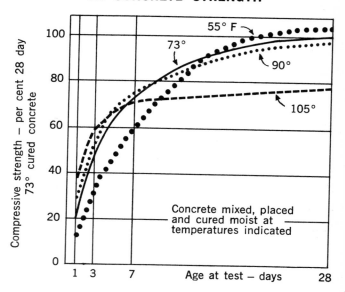

EFFECT OF TEMPERATURE ON CONCRETE STRENGTH

Concrete mixed, placed and cured moist at temperatures indicated

TYPES OF CEMENT

The quality of mortar largely depends on the proportions of the ingredients, especially the proportion of water to cement, the manner in which the mortar is handled and placed after it is mixed, and the thoroughness of the curing. But careful selection of the materials and their proper handling, storing and measuring are also necessary for the best results.

Types of Portland Cement:

Type I: Normal portland cement. This is a general purpose cement suitable for all uses when the special properties of the other types are not required. It is used in pavement and sidewalk construction, reinforced concrete buildings and bridges, railway structures, tanks and reservoirs, sewers, culverts, waterpipe, masonry units, soil-cement mixtures, and for all uses of cement or concrete not subject to special sulfate hazard or where the heat generated by the hydration of the cement will not cause an objectionable rise in temperature.

Type II: Modified portland cement. This cement has a lower heat of hydration than Type I and generates heat at a slower rate. It also has improved resistance to sulfate attack. It is intended for use in structures of considerable size where cement of moderate heat of hardening will tend to minimize temperature rise, as in large piers, heavy abutments and heavy retaining walls when the concrete is placed in warm weather. In cold weather when the heat generated is of advantage, Type I cement may be preferable for these uses. Type II cement is also intended for places where added precaution against sulfate attack is important, as in drainage structures where the sulfate concentrations are higher than normal but are not unusually severe.

Type III: High-early-strength portland cement. This

COMPOSITION OF PORTLAND CEMENT

Type of Portland Cement	Calculated compound composition – per cent				Fineness (Wagner)
	C_3S	C_2S	C_3A	C_4AF	Sq. cm. per gr.
I GENERAL PURPOSE	45	27	11	8	1710
II MODERATE SULFATE RESISTANT	44	31	5	13	1990
III HIGH EARLY STRENGTH	53	19	10	10	2730
IV LOW HEAT	28	49	4	12	1880
V SULFATE RESISTANT	38	43	4	8	1960

EFFECT OF WATER-CEMENT RATIO AND CURING ON PERMEABILITY

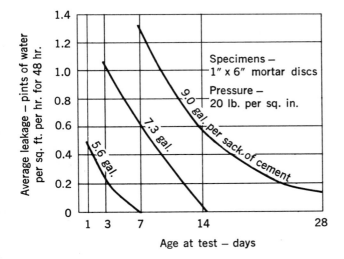

cement is used where high strengths are desired at very early periods. It is used where it is desired to remove forms as soon as possible or to put the concrete into service as quickly as possible, in cold weather construction, to reduce the period of protection against low temperatures, and where high strengths desired at early periods can be secured more satisfactorily or more economically than by using richer mixes of Type I cement.

Type IV: Low-heat portland cement. This is a special cement for use where the amount and rate of heat generated must be kept to a minimum. The development of strength is also at a slower rate. It is intended for use only in large masses of concrete such as large gravity dams where temperature rise resulting from the heat generated during hardening is a critical factor.

Type V: Sulfate-resistant portland cement. This is a special cement intended for use only in structures exposed to severe sulfate action, such as found in some Western states where soils or waters show high alkali content. It has a slower rate of hardening than normal portland cement.

Type of Cement Recommended for Ferro-Cement:

Type 5 is the recommended type. The reason for this is the high alkaline content of salt water; therefore, it is felt that Type 5 will be more impervious to any chemical actions played upon the concrete by salt water.

Sometimes Type 3 is used because of its high strength at an early date. This is used mostly by commercial shops in order to mass produce these hulls. The reason for this is that Type 5 is a slower setting cement. Where a slower type of cement is used, there is a longer period before any more work can be done on the hull as the cement has not gained sufficient strength to withstand the weight of people working on the structure. The high early cement allows people to work on the boat at a much earlier time. The boat can also be moved at a much earlier time, but it must be remembered that alkaline resistance is low in Type 3 cement.

For the builder who is building a single boat, and time is not as critical as in the commercial shop, Type 5 is recommended. This doesn't go off as quickly as Type 3 on the day of application, and allows the more inexperienced person to complete the job before areas of the boat start becoming too stiff to work.

Comparison of Portland Cement:

For practical purposes, portland cements may be considered as being composed of four principal compounds. These are given as follows with their chemical formulas and abbreviations:

Tricalcium silicate	$3CaO.SiO2$	$= C2S$
Dicalcium silicate	$2CaO.SiOa$	$= C2S$
Tricalcium aluminate	$3CaO.A1202$	$= C2A$
Tetracalcium aluminoferrite	$4CaO.A1203.Fe203$	$= C4AF$

The approximate percentage of each compound can be calculated from the chemical analysis. Most of the strength development characteristics are controlled by the C3S and C2S. Together, these compounds usually constitute more than 70 per cent of the whole for most types of cement. The illustration on Page 29 shows typical compound composition data for the five types of portland cement covered by the ASTM specifications. Each value represents the average of four brands of cement of the type indicated.

Concrete made with air-entrained portland cement sometimes has slightly lower strength than corresponding concrete made without an air entrainment additive. In general, each percentage point increase in air content reduces the compressive strength from 3 to 5 per cent and the modulus of rupture from 2 to 3 per cent. The total reduction in compressive strength ordinarily is not more than 10 to 15 per cent and in modulus of rupture 6 to 10 per cent. When the cement factor is maintained constant and the water and sand are reduced as permitted by the improved workability due to the entrained air, there may be little, if any, reduction in strength.

Why Air-Entrainment in Ferro-Cement:

Workability is increased using an air entrainment additive and volume weight is decreased. Both of these factors are desirable in boat work. The amount of concrete applied to a hull should be just sufficient to ensure the spaces in the mesh are completely filled with only enough concrete on the surface to form a protection to the outer layer of mesh. The maximum concrete on the surface should be 1/8″ and the minimum is sufficient to ensure that all the mesh is hidden. Air entrainment greatly aids penetration and the small cells produced by adding air entrainment makes the thin film of concrete on the outside more impenetrable.

In any floating hull which is required to carry a payload, structural weight is of great importance. As boat building materials go, concrete is heavy, but if applied sparingly, not unduly so.

Air entrainment reduces bulk weight about 3 to 5 per cent.

Storage of Cement:

Cement will retain its quality indefinitely if it does not come in contact with moisture. If it is allowed to absorb appreciable moisture it will set more slowly and its strength will be reduced. In storing sacked cement, the warehouse or shed should be as airtight as possible. All cracks in roofs and walls should be closed and there should be no opening between walls and roof. The floor should be above ground to protect it against dampness. Sacks should be stacked close together to reduce circulation of air, but they should not be stacked close against outside walls. If they are to be stored for long periods, the piles should be covered with tarpaulins or other damp-proof covering. Doors and windows should be kept closed.

On smaller jobs where there is no shed or other building in which to store cement, the sacks may be placed on a raised wood platform. Waterproof tarpaulins should be placed over the pile to protect the cement against rain. The tarpaulins should extend over the edges of the platform to prevent rain from collecting on it and thus reaching the bottom sacks.

When sacked cement is in storage for long periods it sometimes acquires what is termed "warehouse pack". This can usually be corrected by rolling the sack on the floor. At the time of use it should be free-flowing and free of lumps. If lumps which cannot be easily broken up are present, the cement should not be used.

Mixing Water:

Water used for mixing mortar should be free of acids, alkalies and oil unless tests or experience indicate that water being considered for use and containing any of these materials is satisfactory. Particularly to be avoided is water containing decayed vegetable matter which may interfere with the setting of the cement. Specifications require that the mixing water be suitable for drinking; such water is usually satisfactory with the possible exception of that from certain small areas where the drinking water contains large amounts of sulphates.

AGGREGATES AND ADMIXTURE

In the following discussion of aggregates it is assumed that the materials used will be from a commercial plant. Even though aggregates are considered as inert materials acting as filler, it has been shown that they constitute some 50 per cent of the volume of the mortar and must meet certain requirements. For most purposes, aggregates should consist of clean, hard, strong and durable particles, free of chemicals or coatings of clay or other fine material that may affect bonding of the cement paste. The contaminating materials most often encountered are dirt, silt, clay, coal, mica, salts, and humus or other organic matter. They may occur as coatings or as loose, fine material. Many of them can be removed by proper washing.

Weak, pliable or laminated aggregate particles are undesirable. Shale, stones laminated with shale, and most cherts are especially to be avoided. Visual inspection will often disclose weaknesses in coarse aggregate. Where doubt exists, the aggregate should be tested.

Particle Shape, Grading and Maximum Size of Aggregate:

Very sharp and rough aggregate particles or flat and elongated particles require more fine material to produce workable concrete than aggregate particles that are more rounded or cubical.

Pozzolan is added to ferro-cement to produce a higher amount of fines than are found in normal concrete. The maximum size of aggregates used should be able to pass a No. 8 mesh. The amount of fines required to pass a 100 mesh should be 15 percent. Fifteen per cent of the total volume of aggregate should be pozzolan, the other 15 per cent should be of a fine silica sand. Pozzolan reacts with any free lime which is found in portland cement, thus making the concrete more salt water resistant as free lime can be dissolved by salt water.

Excellent mortar is made by using crushed stone and other crushed materials but the particles should be more or less cubical in shape. Stones which break up into long slivers should be avoided. Natural sands are usually made up of rounded particles. Sand, made by crushing stone, consists of more angular particles

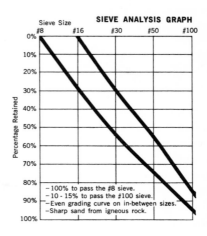

and when used for fine aggregate in mortar, it is essential that those materials having an abundance of thin, sharp and slivery particles be avoided.

The gradation or particle-size distribution of aggregate is determined by a sieve analysis. The standard sieves used for this purpose are numbers 8, 16, 30, 50 and 100 for fine aggregate. These sizes are based on square opening, the size of the openings in consecutive sieves being related by a constant ratio. In grading charts which are convenient for showing size distribution, the lines representing successive sieves are placed at equal intervals.

Fineness modulus is a term often used as an index to the fineness or coarseness of aggregate. It is the summation of the cumulative percentages of the material retained on the standard sieves divided by 100. It is not an indication of grading, for an infinite number of gradings will give the same value for fineness modulus. An example of the calculation of fineness modulus of a sand is given for the following sieve analysis.

	Per Cent Retained (cumulative)
No. 4	2
No. 8	15
No. 16	35
No. 30	55
No. 50	79
No. 100	97
Fineness modulus	= 283 ÷ 100 = 2.83

The grading and maximum size of aggregate are important because of their effect on relative proportions, workability, porosity, and shrinkage. Experience has shown that coarse sands are objectionable, give harsh, unworkable mixes and are hard to finish. In general, aggregates which do not have a large deficiency or excess of any size and give a smooth grading curve produce the most satisfactory results.

	Per Cent Retained (cumulative)
No. 8	0
No. 16	20 to 40
No. 30	40 to 60
No. 50	60 to 70
No. 100	80 to 90

The amount of fine aggregate passing the number 50 and number 100 sieves affects workability, finish, and surface texture, and water gain. Experience has shown that in ferro-cement, the fine aggregate should contain not less than 30 per cent passing the number 50 sieve and at least 10 per cent passing the number 100 sieve. With this minimum amount of fines, the mortar has better workability and is more cohesive. Hence there is less water gain than when lower per cent of fines are present. The presence of adequate fines is more important in the wetter mixes than in stiffer mixes.

Commercial Aggregates:

As stated previously, most of the aggregates sold by commercial producers are washed and screened. Washing is done to remove the deleterious materials. In some instances the sands have been washed more than necessary and the process has removed some of the fine particles that are desirable. By adjustments in the washing process or by recovery of some of the fine material, suitable gradings can be obtained.

It is sometimes necessary to blend material of finer grading with the sand to produce a grading meeting the specifications. Blending must be done by methods that will produce a uniform product. It is best to batch the fine material as a separate aggregate during mixing. In no case should blending be attempted by

placing alternate layers of the coarse and fine materials in stockpiles.

Admixtures:

Admixtures are sometimes used in concrete for a variety of purposes, such as to improve workability, reduce segregation, entrain air, or accelerate setting and hardening. Powdered materials such as diatomaceous earth, pumic, fly ash and hydrated lime provide additional fine material and are used as workability agents, but only a few types of additives are practical for boat construction. Often other ways to avoid bleeding or segregation, harshness and difficulties in placing and finishing can be used; these include properly proportioning the materials, using more cement or more fines in the sand, compacting the mortar by vibration. These alternate methods or combinations of them should be considered when the use of an admixture is under consideration.

Admixtures used to entrain air must be carefully controlled, and it is essential to make certain that: 1) enough air is entrained to accomplish the desired results and, 2) too much air is not entrained to reduce the strength of the concrete unnecessarily. Admixtures should be obtained from reliable producers who can provide a uniform product.

Trial Mixes for Air-Entrenched Concrete:

When air is introduced into a mortar mixture there is some reduction in strength if no changes are made in the mix proportions. However, the volume of mortar is increased by an amount equal to the volume of entrained air, resulting in a reduction of the cement factor. The workability of the mortar is improved because of the larger proportion and better cohesiveness of the mortar. Experience indicates that for equal placeability, the slump of the mortar can be somewhat less than that required for mortar without entrained air. Two parts aggregate to one part cement is about as high a cement-to-aggregate ratio as desirable.

As in designing mixes for mortar without entrained air, mixes for air-entrained mortar should be designed by trial. The same applies for fly ash and pozzolan.

MEASURING MATERIALS

If uniform batches of mortar of proper proportions and consistency are to be secured, it is essential that all ingredients be carefully controlled and accurately measured for each batch. The important effects of the relative proportions of cement and water on all the qualities of mortar show that it is just as necessary to measure the water as the other ingredients. A troublesome factor is the effect of the varying amounts of moisture nearly always present in the aggregates, particularly in natural sand. The amount of free moisture introduced into the mixer with the aggregates must be determined and allowance made if accurate control is to be obtained.

Measuring Cement:

If sacked cement is used the batches of mortar should be of such size that only full sacks are used. If fractional sacks of cement are used they should be weighed for each batch. It is not satisfactory to divide sacks of cement on the basis of volume.

Measuring Water:

Dependable and accurate means for measuring the mixing water are essential.

Any liquid additives should be added to the mixing water. This should be stored in a 45-gallon drum, and the proper proportions of additives added when the drum is completely filled. This will allow a constant check to be maintained on quantity, especially with air-entraining agencies. Where a very small amount is used with each mix, the drum of water should be stirred each time before the liquid is removed.

Measuring Aggregates:

Measurement of aggregates by volume cannot be depended upon except under most careful supervision. A small amount of moisture in fine aggregate, which is nearly always present, causes the aggregate to bulk or fluff up. The amount of bulking varies with the amount of moisture present and the grading; fine sands bulk more than coarse sands for a given amount of moisture. The moisture varies from time to time and only small variations cause appreciable changes in the amount of bulking. For these reasons it has become general practice to weigh the aggregates instead of measuring them by volume. Even if no adjustment is made to compensate for changes in moisture, the results will be much more accurate with weight measurement than with volumetric measurement. Thus, if a mix is being used with 200 lbs. of sand per sack of cement and there is a change of 2 per cent in moisture, the weight of sand to compensate for this change would be 4 lbs. On the other hand, this change in moisture content may require a change of 10 per cent or more in volume.

ALL IN THE MIX

All mortar should be mixed thoroughly until it is uniform in appearance with all ingredients uniformly distributed. It has been found that the suitable mixer is the paddle type used by plasterers. This revolves with a horizontal paddle and can generally hold 2 bags of cement and proportionate aggregate which is usually sufficient to keep the job moving.

Mixers should not be loaded above their rated capacity and should be operated at approximately the speeds for which they are designed. If increased output is needed it should be obtained by a larger mixer or by additional mixers, not by speeding up or overloading the equipment on hand. If the blades of the mixer become worn or become coated with hardened mortar, the mixing action will be less efficient. Badly worn blades should be replaced and hardened mortar should be removed before each run of mortar.

Three quarters of the mixing water should be placed in the mixer first, followed by the cement. This should be thoroughly mixed with the water before the aggregates are added. The fines are added first. Pozzolan, fine sand, coarse sands, and the balance of the water to follow. In case there has been any error in weighing the batches, do not allow the mixer to stall.

The mixer should be thoroughly washed whenever the job stops for coffee, etc.; also be careful to wash out all buckets, shovels, etc. used in handling the mortar.

Remixing Mortar:

The initial set of cement does not ordinarily take place until 2 or 3 hours after it is mixed with water. Fresh mortar that is left standing tends to dry out and stiffen somewhat before the cement sets. Such mortar must not be used.

Test for Grading:

As stated previously, the grading of aggregates may be studied by making sieve analysis tests in which the particles are divided into the various sizes by standard sieves. The analysis should be made in accordance with "Standard Method of Test for Sieve Analysis of Fine Aggregate" (ASTN C136). In addition to determining whether the materials meet specifications, sieve analyses are of assistance in selecting the material to use if several aggregates are available. Materials containing too large a proportion of any one size and with some sizes lacking or in too small quantities should be avoided.

Pumps:

Mortar is sometimes pumped through a steel pump line, the method being of particular advantage in larger boats where a large amount of mortar has to be transported from the mixing site to where it is being placed inside the hull. The equipment includes a heavy single acting horizontal piston type pump of rugged construction. The mortar can be pumped along 600 to 1,000 feet of straight horizontal pipe depending on size of pump and size of pipe. Vertical distances are calculated on the basis of 1-foot vertical equalling 8-feet horizontal. A 90-degree bend is equivalent to 40-feet of horizontal pipe, a 45-degree bend equivalent to 20 feet of horizontal pipe. Concrete having a slump of only ½″ has been pumped successfully but best results are secured where there is a slump of 3″ or more. A constant supply of uniform mortar is necessary for successful operation of the pump. To assist in maintaining uniformity, the hopper feeding the pump is often supplied with an agitator to re-mix the mortar as it is dumped into the hopper.

One of the big disadvantages of using a cement pump on a ferro-cement job is that the relatively small amount of concrete used does not usually warrant the amount of cement delivered by the pump. A build-up of mortar may result and frequent stops are usually required to clear the sand which collects in 90 degree elbows thus slowing down the job. The big advantage to the cement pump is not having to pack the concrete in buckets, etc. and having men walk on the structure, unnecessarily causing distortion of the rods and mesh.

Initial tests with a gunnite gun have shown promising results providing the cedar mold method is used. It is necessary to have a backing behind the final layers of chicken wire to stop distortion when a high pressure of concrete hits the skeletal assembly of rods and chicken wire. It is also necessary to go to a more open mesh than normally used in ferro-cement to allow for better penetration. Consequently, the entire reinforcing should be recalculated to compensate for this larger mesh.

Plastering:

Before plastering, forms should be clean, tight and adequately braced. Care should be taken to see that sawdust, nails, and other debris are removed from the spaces to be plastered. Forms should be moistened prior to the placing of the mortar. Where there has been exposure to the sun for some time it may be necessary to saturate the wood thoroughly to tighten the joints.

Reinforcing steel should be clean and free of loose rust or mill scale at the time mortar is placed. Any coatings of hardened mortar should be removed from the steel.

Preparation of Hardened Mortar:

When fresh mortar is placed on hardened mortar it is desirable to secure good bond and a watertight joint. Certain precautions are necessary to accomplish these results. The hardened mortar should be reasonably rough, clean, and moist and some aggregate particles should be exposed. Any laitance or soft layers of mortar should be removed from the top surface of the hardened mortar.

Old mortar that is to be bonded to new mortar must be thoroughly roughened and cleaned. In most cases it is necessary to cut off the entire surface to expose a new surface satisfactory for bonding.

Vibrators:

Vibrators should not be used to transport mortar laterally over long distances, a practice that is too often allowed. The mortar should be deposited as near its final position as possible.

Vibrators may be powered by electric motor, gasoline engine or compressed air. Electrical pencil vibrators are the type most often used.

Precautions should be taken not to over-vibrate to the point that segregation results. This is especially to be guarded against if the mortar is wetter than necessary. On the other hand, the operator must use caution and judgement to be sure that complete consolidation

is secured without segregation and that no areas are missed. Delayed vibration is not injurious so long as the mortar becomes plastic under the action.

Tests have shown that vibration reduces the air content of air-entrained mortar. In most of these tests the mortar was subjected to more than the normal amount of vibration as the specimens were relatively small. Ordinarily, the normal amount of vibration is not likely to reduce the air content more than about one-half of one per cent.

On the cedar mold method, it is difficult to get 100 per cent penetration on vertical planes even when using a vibrator; consequently, the structure may have to be assembled on a tilting floor if the cedar lining is to be left in. If penetration is doubtful the lining should be stripped out of the inside of the hull and a grout coat sprayed on followed by a coat of plaster to ensure all voids have been filled. When stripping the lining, use wide wooden fox wedges to ease the boards and eliminate damage to the hull. The ends of nails or staples protruding through the shell should be ground off with a disc body grinder.

CURING, PROTECTION AND FINISH

It was shown before that the strength and watertightness of mortar improves with age as long as conditions are favourable for continued hydration of the cement. Other qualities such as resistance to freezing and thawing and weathering are similarly affected. The improvement is rapid at the early stages but continues more slowly for an indefinite period. The conditions required are the presence of moisture and favourable temperature. Fresh mortar contains more than enough water for complete hydration of the cement, but with ferro-cement much of this water will be lost by evaporation unless certain precautions are taken. It was shown also that hydration proceeds at a much slower rate when temperatures are below normal and that there is practically no chemical action when the temperature is near freezing or below. Thus it is seen that mortar should be protected so that moisture is not lost during the early stages of hardening and that it should be kept at a temperature that

will promote hydration. The shell should also be protected against injury. The best protection is to ensure that there is no sagging when the weight of the plaster is applied. A shelter is erected around the boat to protect it from wind. There should be adequate protection against drips on the hull from a leaking roof. Water falling in one spot over a couple of hours will produce serious damage. The foundation under the hull should be sufficient to bear the weight without settling.

Mortar can be kept moist by a number of methods such as sprinkling and use of moisture-retention covers or by a seal coat applied as a liquid which hardens to form a thin membrane. In hot, dry weather, wood forms will dry out and should be kept moist by sprinkling. In all cases, exposed surfaces must be protected from moisture loss. To facilitate bonding a muriatic acid wash should be given to the hull to etch the surface and this should be neutralized with caustic soda. The surface is wetted thoroughly and while still wet is scrubbed vigorously with a 5 to 10 per cent solution of muriatic acid with stiff bristle brushes. The acid is removed by flushing with clean water. The same procedure should be repeated with a 5 to 10 per cent solution of caustic soda and this should be thoroughly flushed with clean water. These steps should be taken just before painting and after all sanding with a carborundum brick has been completed. This wash coat completely removes all traces of loose grit and any curing agents that may still be left on the surface. It also puts minute pits into the shell, thus allowing an excellent bond for the finish.

Where mortar is kept moist by sprinkling, care should be taken to prevent drying of the surfaces between applications of water. Alternate cycles of wetting and drying of green mortar are conducive to crazing or cracking of the surface. A fine spray of water applied continuously provides a more constant supply of moisture and is better than copious applications of water with periods of drying between.

Moisture-retaining covers such as burlap or cotton quilts are also used. Care should be taken to cover the entire hull.

Sealing curing compounds are available in black, colourless or white pigmented coatings. Some of them are applied in one coat but two coats will give better results. The application should be made immediately the plastering has been finished. If there is any delay, the mortar should be kept moist until the application is made.

As shown previously, temperature affects the rate at which the chemical reactions between cement and water take place; consequently, it affects the rate at which the mortar hardens, the increases in strength and it improves other qualities. In hot weather, certain precautions should be taken to avoid high temperatures in the fresh mortar and attention to curing is even more important than under normal conditions to avoid rapid drying. High temperatures in the fresh mortar cause rapid stiffening.

Any mortar dropped on the wire and allowed to go hard before plastering commences in the area can cause voids in the structure. This must be avoided. Any mortar dropped should be immediately cleaned up and the area washed off completely, thus allowing the mortar to penetrate the area easily when the area is plastered.

In cold weather construction, it is often necessary to heat the materials and to cover the green shell or to provide a heated enclosure.

In ferro-cementing, the placing temperature should be 50-70 degrees F. In no case should the materials be heated to the point that the temperature of the fresh mortar is above 70 degrees F. This results in lower strength.

In relatively mild weather, that is when the temperature is generally above 40-45 degrees F. with only short periods below this range, heating only the mixing water will usually be sufficient to provide the desired temperature in the mortar. More heat units can be stored in the water than in the other materials and it is also the most convenient material to heat. The average specific heat (heat units required to raise temperature of 1 lb. of material 1 degree F.) of the solid materials

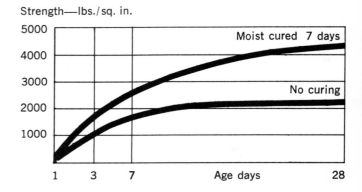

EFFECTS OF CURING

Strength—lbs./sq. in.

may be assumed to be 0.22 compared to 1.00 for water. Mixing water is best heated in auxiliary tanks by an oil-burning heater. The water should not be heated above 165 to 175 degrees F. because of the possibility of causing quick or "flash" set of the cement.

After mortar is in place, it should be kept at a favourable temperature long enough to avoid injury by exposure to the atmospheric temperature. In general, it is required that the air surrounding the shell be maintained at 70 degrees F. or above. Protection against low temperature must be extended for a full curing period of 28 days.

In extremely hot weather, extra care is required to avoid high temperatures in the fresh mortar and to prevent rapid drying of the newly placed mortar.

While the mortar is still plastic, the surface is

floated with wood, cork or metal floats. In this process, the surface is brought to true grade, any high spots are cut down and low spots filled in, and sufficient grout is brought to the surface to produce the desired finish. Caution should be taken not to overwork the mortar while it is still plastic as this may bring an excess of grout to the surface. An excess of fine material at the surface should be avoided, particularly as it may scale or dust off later.

Where floating is done to provide a coarse texture as the final finish, it may be necessary to float the surface a second time after it has partially hardened so that the desired finish can be produced and the surface will retain it.

A scored surface is sometimes produced by brooming the mortar before it has hardened thoroughly. A rough scoring is produced by the use of a steel wire broom or one made from stiff coarse fibers similar to the push brooms used for street cleaning. The brooming is done after the surface has been floated. The mortar is troweled once to a smooth surface and then broomed with a hair brush. Brooming should be done after the mortar is hard enough to retain the scoring.

Brooming is done in bilges where ballast is to be added later. This facilitates the bond. It can also be done to decks to give non-skid surfaces but it is not advisable as it is often too coarse and could cause injury should someone fall on it at sea.

Where rubbing is required, the first rubbing is done with coarse carborundum stones when the shell is hard enough to prevent aggregate being pulled out by the operation. The shell is then cured until final rubbing is done with finer stones. The mortar worked up by the rubbing or mortar applied to assist rubbing should not be spread in a thick layer over the shell, nor should it be used to fill large depressions. All of this mortar should be removed or it will weather off later and produce a blotchy appearance. The shell should be damp when rubbing is done and should be kept damp for a day or two to cure any mortar left on the surface.

After the hull surface has been etched with muriatic acid, it is advisable to apply two coats of epoxy resin. The first coat will soak into the shell and the second will flow over the entire boat, producing a glossy effect. This serves the purpose of completely sealing the exterior of the hull with a very durable sealer and also gives a coating to any stray strands of chicken wire that may have been bared by rubbing. This should prevent any messy rust streaks running down the hull sides once the boat has been exposed to the salt water for several years. Epoxy is best applied with a roller thus giving a slightly dappled finish.

High gloss finishes should be avoided on cement hulls as a rounded area of this size is extremely difficult to fair completely. If a high gloss paint is applied, the slightest flat or hollow will show up quite noticeably in the sunlight. In contrast, the textured finish left by the roller is ideal.

Epoxy paint should be applied over the epoxy resin as this will give the best bond. Several coats should be applied as directed by the manufacturer. If there are too many flat spots on the hull and a perfect finish is desired, a thin layer of polyester based body filler can be skimmed over the hull before applying the epoxy, and this can be sanded down to the desired finish. Rotary disc type sanders with flexible backings are most desirable for this operation. As putty will fill the sandpaper very quickly and render it useless, these discs can be removed and slapped against the hull to clean the putty out of the paper. An average grit is recommended, something in the neighborhood of 80 grit carborundum paper. If a disc grinder is not available, a cork sanding block should be used employing wet and dry carborundum paper. This paper can be dipped in a bucket of water and kept clean. Also the water used in sanding helps lubricate the surface thus making the sanding more uniform.

A very fine finish can be achieved this way, similar to the finish of fine china. The paint should be applied with a pure bristle brush and each coat lightly sanded. In general, the finish that can be achieved on a concrete boat is usually superior to other one-of-a-kind building methods, providing that care is exercised through all phases of construction.

The exterior of a concrete hull is watertight without the epoxy coat and can be painted with an oil based exterior paint.

It is now important to look at some of the other materials which will go into the construction of the ferro-cement boat. In particular, wood, reinforcing bar and mesh or chicken wire all play an equal role in the building process.

Wood itself covers a tremendous field and a brief summary of its role is certainly called for. Here we are indebted to N. B. Hutcheon and J. H. Jenkins who prepared a paper on the subject for the Canadian Building Digest.

Launching day is close at hand for two more beautifully finished ferro-cement boats in this New Zealand yard.

CHAPTER 6

A LOOK AT WOOD

The following information will help you understand some of the characteristics of wood.

It explains why wood is such a good building material generally and why care should be used in selecting the type of wood and to determine if wood itself actually contains the properties you require.

Basically wood is light, strong, and easy to work but it is not the strongest material. Fastening wood is sometimes difficult. Metal can be welded, fiberglass patched, but wood takes much more preparation. Wood is prone to dry rot and teredo worm but plays a very important role in ferro-cement construction because of its many versatile qualities.

Many of the applications and practices in the use of wood have become established through long experience. This basis for predicting performance can be inadequate or even misleading when certain conditions are involved, unless the reasons for satisfactory past performance can be identified and related to new situations. It is thus important with wood, as with other materials, to understand basic properties and their characteristics in use in order to be able to select and to design with confidence.

The outstanding characteristic of wood, apart from its general availability, workability and relatively low cost, is its ability to withstand both tensile and compressive stresses along the grain. It can thus withstand bending loads, and it is this capability that makes it unique among natural structural materials. As this superior strength in tension and compression is along the grain, the length of the structural members obtainable is limited only by the height of the tree or by the length of log that can be handled. The appropriateness of the diameter to length ratio (often the whole trunk can be used as a structural member) is a reflection of the natural function of the trunk in supporting the tree.

The markedly reduced strength properties across the grain and in shear along it introduce some interesting features to the use of wood for general mast purposes. While these are well recognized and are taken into account in timber engineering practice, it is well to review some of them in the interest of understanding wood.

Wooden masts themselves present little problems since they can carry axial compression well. When high concentrated loads are transferred to a post, local crushing in the cross-grain direction becomes a possibility and must always be checked in view of the reduced compressive strength in this direction.

Short wood beams, which can, because of their short span, carry high transferse loads and consequently have high induced shear stresses, must be checked for horizontal shear failure in the long-grain direction. The proportionately low shear strength along the grain also makes it necessary to design carefully when exploiting the generally excellent tensile properties of wood in tension members because complications are introduced into the transfer of end loads. Splices in tension members and on the tension side of beams require similar attention. Long-scarf joints, relatively long gusset or butt blocks become necessary in order to provide the areas necessary for load transfer by shear. For the same reason, bolts or nails used in such fastenings must always be located at adequate distances from the ends of the members. When large tension loads must be transferred at an angle to one member, it is usually necessary to use intermediate elements such as gusset plates or hanging knees to assist in distributing the load without exceeding the permissible stresses in tension across the grain.

There can be appreciable deformation with time, and failure can occur at lower loads when they are to be resisted continuously over long periods. Correspondingly, higher loads can be carried over short periods. This tendency under stress for continuing deformation, or creep, which occurs under certain conditions with most materials, is not always a disadvantage. It can lead to some desirable relief of stresses such as those caused by changes in moisture content.

The most significant effect of moisture content on wood is related to the dimensional changes that take place with changes in moisture content. The marked difference between small moisture-induced movements along the grain and those across the grain introduces some important considerations.

It may be noted that shrinkage along the grain, upon drying from a fibre saturation level of about 30 per cent to oven-dry, may be only about 0.1 per cent, while across the grain it can be as high as five per cent. Shrinkage in the tangential direction is greater than that in the radial direction. Wood put in place at a relatively high moisture content of say 19 per cent could readily dry to a moisture content of five per cent or even less, shrinking as much as 2½ per cent or ¼-inch in the width of a 10-inch board.

Fortunately the corresponding change along the grain, that is, along the length of the board, will only be about 1/50 of this amount.

The fact that such changes occur in cross-grain directions is significant, however, and must always be kept in mind. Interior partitions fastened structurally to an outside cabin side may not change by similar amounts or at the same time. Vertical members built into the bulkhead do not change in the same way and must be provided with suitable clearances to avoid having the planks being pried apart when shrinkage takes place. If this is not done all such members may be heavily loaded when shrinkage takes place. It must always be specially arranged to avoid the conflict from differential changes in dimension if difficulties are to be avoided, or unprocessed state is affected potentially by the tendency to relatively large cross-grain dimensional change when every significant moisture content change in service can be expected. Consider, for example, that every structural connection in wood, with the possible exception of a glued joint, can be affected in its performance by differential dimensional changes in the members.

Even simple glued joints, including those in laminated wood members show shrinkage or swelling stresses if the pieces being put together do not have identical moisture response properties. **Therefore, it is very important in boat work when joining two pieces of wood to use a mechanical bond such as a screw or a through bolt as well as glue but it must be remembered when calculating the strength of joint, only the glue or the bolts may be calculated; they cannot be added together although one does help the other.**

Basically a bolt helps a glue joint by acting as a clamp when the joint is put together and a glue joint helps a bolted surface by remaining absolutely rigid and does not allow any stress to be put on the bolt except the stress of the wood itself expanding.

It is possible that the bolt may be loosened as the wood expands and contracts. Nevertheless, experience has shown a through bolt fastening gives a superior bond and if a through bolt is strategically installed in conjunction with glue the joint is very strong indeed.

Every dimension across grain in wood and every dimension of any wood structure that includes cross-grain wood is subject to change with variations in moisture content unless this is prevented by some form of restraint. Under such restraint stresses will always be produced. All successful applications of wood must take into account the dimensional change characteristics of wood due to moisture.

Wood taken from outdoor storage to be used in the interior joinery usually adjusts to a lower moisture content in service. If it is fastened in place at outdoor moisture content, there will be an initial shrinkage as well as a subsequent shrinkage and swelling owing to in-service conditions. The influence of initial shrinkage may be avoided if the moisture content can be adjusted to the level it will subsequently have in service before the wood is put in place.

It is always preferable to use wood that is at least as dry as properly protected outdoor storage will provide. In some situations, particularly with joinery, flooring and other interior building applications where shrinkage must be minimized in the interests of good performance, wood may have to be kiln dried in order to achieve the desirable reduction in moisture content prior to manufacture or application. Moisture content as low as eight per cent, or even six per cent in some cases, as for fir flooring, is commonly provided through kiln drying. Such drying is of little benefit, however, if the wood is allowed to return to higher levels of moisture content before use. Swelling can also be a problem for example, in wood flooring tightly laid at a moisture content. It may, in extreme cases, buckle or shift with a rise in moisture content.

There are, then, some limitations but also some excellent possibilities for minimizing dimensional change problems by controlling the moisture content of wood at the time it is put into service. It may also be possible, within limits, to select species having relatively small dimensional change characteristics. Cedar, for example, is relatively stable dimensionally across the grain and thus may be a preferred material for solid wood exterior planking. Improvement may be achieved also in planking by selecting a preferred grain direction, as with quarter-cut or edge-grain planking, which takes advantage of the lower dimensional change in the radial as compared with the tangential grain direction.

Such possibilities, including the use of coatings to reduce the rate of response to short-time changes in conditions of exposure, serve only to emphasize the need to recognize that dimensional changes will take place consistent with imposed conditions and the basic nature of wood. It is necessary to design realistically for them, in both engineering and architectural applications if consistently good performance is to be achieved.

Some processed forms of wood are of interest in the context of these discussions. Wood can be broken down by pulping or chipping and reconstituted into sheets in numerous ways as represented by paper, fibreboards and chipboards of various kinds. The strength and the dimensional change properties in the different directions of the sheet or board are altered in ways that are generally quite consistent with the nature of the fibre reorientation achieved.

When the fibres are laid in more or less random fashion in the plane of the finished board, some of the properties in the two principal directions of the board become more nearly equal at values between those for the long and cross-grain directions of the original wood. Dimensional changes from the wet to dry condition in plywoods will normally be in the range of ¼ to ½ per cent in width and length directions. Changes in thickness may be greater, approximately those in the original cross-grain direction.

Plywood is one of the more interesting forms of processed wood. As the geometry of the fibre orientation in the board is clearly defined — alternating grain directions in successive veneers at right angles— reasonably adequate calculations of the properties of the composite board can often be made. Plywood for general use must always be of balanced construction. Briefly, this means that each veneer on one side of a sheet must be balanced by one of equal properties and equal orientation on the other side. Unless this is done serious warping will take place when the moisture content changes.

A three-ply board with three equal plies provides balanced construction, but it has unequal properties along and across it because there are two long-grain plies in one direction, only one in the other. This directional effect is progressively reduced as the number of plies is increased.

The strength of the board in tension or compression is determined largely by the percentage of long grain in the cross-section being loaded and by the long-grain properties of the original wood. The situation in bending is somewhat more complex; not only the grain direction but also the position of the veneers in relation to the surface of the sheet are involved.

Shear properties in the plane of the sheet are always greatly improved because of the reinforcement given by adjacent plies against tension failure across the grain. The improvement in dimensional stability is marked, since the superior stability and modulus of elasticity along the grain provide an enhanced restraint for the cross-grain dimensional change.

It is appropriate in concluding this discussion to refer briefly to the durability of wood. As wood is organic in nature it can be attacked and destroyed by micro-organisms of various kinds. The risk generally becomes serious when wood is maintained at a high moisture content in excess of 20 per cent but less than saturated. Treatment with preservatives is usually desirable in order to extend its life under these conditions. Wood can have a very long life when continuously immersed in water. At the other end of the moisture scale, it can last almost indefinitely if protected from sunlight and from excessive moisture content. Sunlight slowly attacks and changes the exposed surface, but its main deteriorating effect is probably associated with the rapid large moisture changes and corresponding dimensional changes that can result in serious checking when exposed wood is wetted by rain and then dried by sun heat.

Here then we have emphasized some of the potentially challenging aspects of wood and its applications. This has been done intentionally, and without any thought of being critical of wood as a material, but in order to promote a better understanding of its nature and of the ways in which it will perform in particular situations. It is only through such understanding that the best ways of using it can be devised and unsuitable performance avoided.

Now we must look at another vital material used in the ferro-cement boatbuilding process — reinforcing bar.

Wood plays a very important role in ferro-cement boat construction.

Facing page: With spinnaker set, "Swanhilde" heads out for the open water.

The reinforcing rods—a very important factor in construction.

CHAPTER 7

REINFORCING BAR

The reinforcing bar like the concrete and chicken wire plays a vital part in ferro-cement construction. There are many types of reinforcing rods available and we will discuss a few of these and their manufacturing process to give a better idea of the type to use.

Basically the reinforcing bar acts in the following way: Initially it acts as a spacer between the layers of chicken wire. It also gives shape to the boat during construction. The rod itself acts under tension as a strength member. As concrete is only strong under compression, it assists the hull to withstand stresses from chain plates (tension stress) and the general movement of a boat in the seaway. It helps the boat to withstand impact.

A few points must be remembered when using rebar. All joints must be properly lapped to make the reinforcing a continuous rod. Ends of rod should not be buried in the hull. Where rods don't end at a skreed, they should be taken alongside another rod and tied or welded for at least one foot. Care should be taken to avoid kinking the rods while handling. When a stressed rod of high carbon content is used, care should be exercised with heating, welding and bending.

Generally speaking, a high carbon stressed rod is the best for ferro-cement construction. It is springy and stiff, helps maintain firm lines throughout construction and stretches very little when put under tension. This is the ideal but this type of rod is very difficult to work with. For the latter reason a low carbon wire which has not been stress-relieved or annealed is more practical. It is stiff enough to give most of the desired qualities mentioned earlier and yet is flexible enough for difficult bending. Any ferro-cement boat construction can be accomplished using this rod.

Cold rolled reinforcing bar sometimes used in ferro-cement boat-building has a low carbon content. There is, however, very little springiness in this bar and it is easily bent if heavy loads are imposed. It is further liable to stretch causing a slight crack in the shell itself.

Tension must be transferred to the rebar instantly, and consequently it should be placed in such a manner that it lies directly in line with the area under stress. It should not lie at an angle to this stress or the full benefit of the rod will not come into play.

In designing rods into a boat, these areas of stress must be carefully observed and the bars laid-up properly. Joints of intersecting rods should be connected. This will help shorten the length of pull on the rod and transfer this slightly to other rods in the immediate area. The aim is to use a lot of rods finely dispersed. Concrete acts differently in the immediate vicinity of steel than in mass, taking on some of the properties of the metal.

Inside the part-finished hull, chicken wire is laid over the rod and pipe framework. Note wooden scaffold for ease of working.

CHAPTER 8

SOME FACTS ABOUT WIRE

Here the authority is the American Iron and Steel Institute and the following are excerpts from their publication "Wire Rods and Carbon Steel".

Carbon Steel:

Steel is considered to be carbon steel when no minimum content is specified or required for aluminum, boron, chromium, cobalt, columbium, molybdenum, nickel, titanium, tungsten, vanadium or zirconium or any other element added to obtain a desired alloying effect; when the specified minimum for copper does not exceed 0.40 per cent; or when the maximum content specified for any of the following elements does not exceed the percentage noted: manganese 1.65, silicon 0.60, copper 0.60.

In all carbon steel small quantities of certain residual elements, unavoidably retained from raw materials, are sometimes found which are not specified or required, such as copper, nickel, molybdenum, chromium, etc. For many applications, those elements are not important.

The Steel Ingot:

The steel ingot has been designed to meet a variety of conditions of manufacture. Research and manufacturing experience extending over the greater part of a century has resulted in the production of many shapes and sizes.

The cross section of most ingots approximates a square or rectangle with rounded corners. The height or length of the ingot is always greater than the cross-sectional dimensions. All ingots are tapered and are cast either big-end up or big-end down.

Regardless of the size or shape of the ingot, steel is subject to internal variations in chemical composition and homogeneity due to natural phenomena which occur as the steel solidifies. The size of the ingot influences the character and magnitude of such variations. The following general discussion of this subject is set forth in the interest of a fuller understanding of an important component material in the ferro-cement boat.

There are four general types of steel. They are killed, semi-killed, capped and rimmed. In the case of killed ingots, and to a lesser degree in semi-killed and capped ingots, because of shrinkage during solidification, a central cavity known as pipe forms in the ingot as the last of the metal solidifies. Primary pipe is located in the upper portion of the ingot. Under some conditions a shrinkage cavity, known as secondary pipe, may form in the ingot below, but not connected with, the primary pipe. Secondary pipe normally welds in rolling. Rimmed steel ingots may contain also a small shrinkage cavity, but generally the top portion is porous and spongy because of evolution of gas during solidification.

The phenomenon of selective freezing, which is

47

associated with the solidification of steel, results in segregation and causes non-uniformity in chemical composition within the ingot. Given portions of the solidified metal may contain either more or less of the elements originally contained in the liquid steel. Segregation in varying degrees is found in all types of steel ingot. The principal factors affecting the amount of segregation are the type and composition of steel, the casting temperature, the ingot shape and size, and the inherent segregating characteristics of the elements being considered.

Carbon is the principal hardening element in steel, and as carbon increases the hardness of steel increases. Tensile strength also increases as the carbon increases up to about 0.85 per cent carbon in wire. Ductility and weldability decrease with increasing carbon.

The surface quality becomes impaired as the carbon content increases in rimmed steels. By contrast, killed steels have poorer surface in the lower carbon grades. Carbon segregates within the ingot, and, because of its major effect on properties, carbon segregation is frequently of more significance and importance than the segregation of other elements.

Wire rods are hot rolled from billets to an approximate round cross section. They are produced in coils in one continuous length. Wire rods are not comparable to hot rolled bars in accuracy of cross section or surface finish because of the methods of manufacture. Wire rods are a semi-finished product and are intended primarily for the manufacture of wire.

Wire rod sizes are designated by fractional or decimal parts of an inch or by the gauge numbers of the Steel Wire Gauge.

In the production of wire a rod, which is a coiled hot rolled product approximately round in cross section, is drawn through the tapered hole of a die or a series of dies. The smallest size of hot rolled rod commonly made is 7/32 inches (nominal 0.218 in. diameter). Sections smaller than this are produced by cold work, the number of dies employed depending upon the finished diameter required. To start the drawing, one end of the rod is pointed, inserted through the die and attached to a power-driven block which pulls the rod through the die and coils the resultant wire.

In summation, the rods start off as an ingot and are rolled and drawn through a series of dies until the desired size is reached. During the cold drawing process as the rod decreases in size it increases in pounds per square inch tensile strength and becomes stiffer. When the rods are passed through a galvanizing process or an annealing process they are stressed-relieved and become softer, decreasing in their tension strength per square inch. Thus a low carbon hard drawn wire is much stronger and springier before galvanizing. Although the galvanizing process affords some measure of protection from salt water action, it also weakens the rod.

In ferro-cement construction the rod is generally placed in the centre of the structure sufficiently covered by mortar. This offers the same protection as galvanizing. The mortar used is of a very dense nature, and is waterproof. The galvanizing process is therefore of little value. It is only of assistance in steel areas which come in direct contact with the surface and are exposed.

Chicken wire is made by the same process as reinforcing bar only it is taken a few steps further. Once the rod is drawn to the desired size, it is stress relieved and put through a machine which twists it into mesh with an hexagonal shape. This shape is very desirable for stretching over the many compound curves found in a boat hull. The mesh, chicken wire or bird netting is manufactured using two processes. One sees the wire stress relieved by a galvanizing action and then manufactured into rolls. The other is stress relieved using a heat process before being manufactured into mesh and then hot-dipped galvanized. This second process tends to solder the joints tight and make the wire quite stiff to use. Both types are good in ferrocement. It has been found that wire which is galvanized after manufacture is better for the gentle curves of the hull. It is stiffer and consequently can be applied tighter. For edges around the stem, sheer and deadwood areas, the pre-galvanized wire is superior. It is more easily formed to take the rapidly changing shapes in these areas. The joints are loose and the wire is more easily distorted. This saves cutting darts into the chicken wire, a practice which must be avoided wherever possible. When the chicken wire is manufactured a factory edge is left on the edges of the roll. This does away with stray ends of wire. If these stray ends are exposed by cutting they will tend to spring out and show on the surface of the hull after plastering. There, they rust and leave unsightly streaks running down the topsides of the boat and also form voids along which moisture can travel to the interior of the cement causing further corrosion.

Chicken wire can be obtained in an ungalvanized state but because of its close proximity to the surface of the shell, it is not recommended. As all chicken wire is stress relieved before manufacture, there is very little difference in strength between the galvanized and ungalvanized types. The part that chicken wire plays in ferro-cement construction is equal in degree to the part played by the reinforcing bar and mortar. The wire gives a very fine distribution of steel right at the surface of the shell thus helping to avoid surface cracks in the mortar. But this wire must be applied as tightly as possible. Being six-sided, it has very little strength under tension unless snug in all directions. It is essential to fasten this wire at many points until the entire surface of the mesh applied to the hull is taut.

Care must be taken to avoid too many layers of chicken wire in any one area or penetration will become difficult at this point. If more strength is required in a certain area, it should be provided by additional reinforcing bar. The chicken wire serves only a limited purpose—prevention of initial grazing on the skin surface. Again it cannot be stressed too strongly that perfect penetration is essential. Voids left in the mortar are potential trouble spots for corrosion and they are areas which, when the rod is put under tension, will cause an unevenness of the work load. When the steel is put under tension, surface friction develops between the steel and the mortar. The mortar near the surface of the steel is put into compression. This breaks down where there is a void in the shell and imposes a much heavier workload on the steel in this area. This could easily result in a structural failure. Steel and mortar expand and contract at much the same rate, and the surface bond will be maintained throughout the life of the structure unless it has received a severe blow in a local area. If there is damage to the surface of the hull and cracks appear, the mortar should be pounded out using two heavy objects on either side of the hull. These are hammered together to cause a pulverizing action. All the loose mortar is removed until there is no sign of surface breakdown in the bond. The area is then thoroughly cleaned and new mortar applied.

Care is taken to ensure that the new mortar has a good bond with the old and with the old steel bared by the pulverizing action. All traces of mortar must be removed from the surfaces of the wire, with care taken to avoid distortion. This would leave the wire loose and stretched.

We have now covered the manufacturing process of cement, the grading of sand and aggregates, the manufacture of steel and chicken wire, and have explained the part each material plays in the whole. Once a good understanding of this is obtained, the material should be reread. A complete understanding will allow any intelligent man to do modifications to existing hull designs as to shape of the craft. Perhaps in 10 or 20 years ferro-cement boats will have adopted many additional shapes, will be still stronger to withstand even greater impacts and to further improve on the existing good qualities of plasticity and versatility.

It is hoped that development of this fine boat building material will be helped by serious co-operation and exchange of ideas at this stage so that ferro-cement will achieve its optimum results. No one person has all the answers. It would be wise to pool information, and for those entering commercial building of craft by this process to be those who can assemble data correctly and streamline their manufacturing processes. It has been proven over and over again that everyone gains through co-operation and exchange of ideas. We cannot do better than follow the example of Professor Nervi who shared his findings with the world, and who alone should be given the credit for furthering development of the amazing boat building material called ferro-cement.

An excellent quality of finish is shown in this 45-foot ferro-cement launch owned by New Zealand's Jeff Entrican.

CHAPTER 9

HOW TO BUILD THE BOAT

You've taken the big step. You've joined the ranks of ferro-cement boat builders. Here, in the following pages are all the step-by-step instructions which will lead you to your first day of sailing in your own craft.

Unfortunately, as in any boat construction project, there are no short cuts that will get you to your destination quickly. Building a boat is a rewarding experience and right at the outset you must decide to go the route first-class. If you skimp and try to save you will probably come to regret it some day. That is why we start off these instructions with the first real major step to be taken by any amateur builder — establishing an ideal place to work.

Obviously the perfect spot is to get a boat-shed on the water. It will save you costs of transportation at a later date, but alas a boatshed by the water is hard to come by. In common with most other amateur builders you will probably have to settle for a shed in your backyard and we will have to assume that you live in an area where sheds are permitted. You are going first class so your shed, wherever it is located, must be a good one, solid and more than big enough for the project.

The shed size required as a minimum has a 6-foot clearance under the rafters to enable the boat to be jacked up onto a trailer after construction and this will also give you the necessary headroom to work on the topsides.

There should be at least 4-foot clearance at either side of the shed, leaving room for work benches and scaffolding.

The shed should be 20-feet longer than the boat so there is room to store materials and a place for table saw, etc.

Do not skimp on the size of the shed. Building a boat is a big project and if done in your spare time might take as much as two years or so to complete. The little extra money spent here will pay off in building time, and will generally reflect the quality of the work which goes into the boat. If the materials are properly stored they will not be weathered before finished. They will last much longer and finish better. With sufficient room to stand back and view the job as it progresses any unfairness will be detected before it is too late to correct.

There should be a solid foundation under the boat so it does not change throughout construction. There should be a wood floor around the boat to help keep the shop clean, stop tools from being lost or dulled when dropped on concrete. A good work bench should be built along one side· of the shop. Allow as much window space as possible and a door large enough to get bulky materials through. Put in two strings of lights so there are not any dark places while working at night. The concrete boat is very dark before painting and absorbs a lot of light. Put in plug-ins of sufficient amperage to take any power tools you will be using.

There are three types of structures which are good. The best is the rigid frame and plans for this are available free from the Plywood Manufacturers Association of British Columbia at 1477 West Pender Street, Room 310, Vancouver, Canada.

The second is a more conventional type building covered in sheathing or plastic. This has several disadvantages. The plastic is very cold in the winter and hot in the summer. Whenever the wind blows it becomes very distracting in the plastic shed. If one builds conventionally there must be sufficient pitch to the roof to get rid of snow. Normally a 5-in-12 pitch is minimum. A "W" truss will do well here. The third is merely a framework to support the boat, over which a plastic cover may be thrown in order to keep off the rain. The disadvantages of this type are obvious.

TOOLS

Concrete boat building requires very few tools, compared with conventional wooden boat construction. The tools needed to build the cement hull include:

Either a hickey or plumbers pipe vice (3-legged) or some other arrangement for bending pipe

Carborundum drills	Hack saw
Pliers	Welder
Pipe cutters	Bolt cutters for cutting the reinforcing bars
Steel drills	
Cold chisel	

The welder, pipe vice, bolt cutters and pipe cutters are needed for a short time only and are probably best rented or borrowed.

The essential power tools for finishing the wood working and shed construction are:

Hand power saw   Table saw

Electric drill   Belt sander
(at least ⅜")

These tools will enable the builder to do a satisfactory job on the woodworking. If a better finish is required other tools which will be helpful are:

Router   Jointer   Band saw—12"

The essential kit of hand tools are:

1—8 point saw	Chisels ¼" ½" 1" 2"
1—10 point saw	Good oil stone
Key hole saw	16 oz. hammer, good quality
Brace and assorted bits	
Smoothing plane	Large ratchet screw driver and attachments
Plumb bob	
Level	Carpenter's rafter square and "T" square
Nail sets	
Bevel gauge	Set socket wrenches
4—12" clamps	12' tape and 3' ruler
Block plane	

BUILDING THE BOAT

You now have your place to build and the tools are at hand—the real work is beginning. And, as in all boat construction, the first job, that of lofting, is the most important. It cannot be stressed too strongly how vital this stage is to the final outcome of your project.

If you have any doubts about your ability to loft out the boat efficiently it would be advisable to pay a visit to your local library and take out a couple of books on the subject. There are many good books available and our own book on backyard boat building will be found particularly valuable.

You must remember that in building a cement boat, you are bending your frames in half-inch water pipe

from the loftings, and this does not leave you the same margin of error as in a wooden construction. In the normal wooden boat you can correct discrepancies by packing out or shaving down the timber. In the water pipe, you have to be right first time or the faults will show in the lines of your boat.

Bearing in mind that lofting is the major step in the construction—even professional boat-builders will spend a couple of weeks ensuring that their lines are perfect—we now look at the table of offsets. Here, the designer has used the outside line of the boat's shell to calculate weight, displacement and line.

This means you must subtract three-quarters-of-an

inch (to allow for hull thickness) from the offset measurements. Some plans have this correction already made but this could not be done in the cement-boat projects. With two different methods of construction available, two different corrections are offered.

If, for example, you have decided to build your boat using the cedar mold method, then you will have to subtract one-and-a-half inches from your water lines thus allowing for the additional thickness of the wooden lining and vapor barrier.

Again, read these points carefully. *Allow three quarters of an inch if you are building in the conventional pipe and chicken wire way and one-and-a-half inches if you are using the cedar mold method.* Do these things right the first time and you will save yourself hours and hours of unnecessary labor later on.

With all these points firmly in mind, we turn to the actual lofting. This should all be done full size so it is obvious you are going to need a large area. Your boatshed is certainly the ideal spot providing you have ensured that the floor is perfectly level. You will need extra space in which to swing the battens used in establishing the curves. So, clear the area completely before you start the job. Ideally you should have a 10-foot clearance over the full length of the boat and enough width to allow you to get both baselines in with ease. It also helps to establish the centre line of the boat exactly where the boat is going to sit when construction begins.

Remember, all you are attempting to do is to transfer the two-foot picture of the boat before you to its full-size on your shed floor. But again it cannot be stressed too strongly—*you must be accurate.* The thickness of a pencil line on the small plan can be as much as three-eighths or even half-an-inch when transferred to full size.

To start with, strike up your center line on the floor and from this you can set your parallel base lines. All these lines should be struck with a chalk line and pencilled in later, using a straight edge. Next the stations are marked off and, using a large square, these are extended to above the sheer line. The edge of a piece of 4x8 can be used here as your square. At each end station you now mark in your water lines, and join these with a chalk line. What you now virtually have is a large grid on which you will draw your boat full-size. Spare a few minutes to check again that all your measurements are correct. The best check is to measure across your 'grid pattern' diagonally. The two measurements should be the same if you're all square.

Next step is to mark in your buttock, diagonal and sheer lines as marked on the lines plan. These are marked on each of your stations and joined up by using a batten. An ideal batten is a piece of one-inch-and-a-quarter by three-quarters which is five feet longer than the boat at each end. More difficult curves can be established by using a thinner batten, say three-quarters by three-quarters, of any straight-grained wood. Nails driven into the floor between the station points will allow you to bend the batten to the different curves before firmly pencilling in the line with a carpenter's pencil.

The radius of the transom is now drawn in before moving on to the profile. The profile is superimposed over the established lines and it is advisable to use a different colored pencil to avoid confusion. Measuring up from the base line, mark in the sheer, stem keel bottom, stern and rudder and again, join up the lines with a batten. Next comes the section shapes and these are established by measuring out from the center station of the loft. Remember that this shows you half the boat looking from aft and half from looking forward. Here you run into more complex curves and you may have to use a three-eighths square batten.

This completes your lofting of the hull. Step back and check that everything is in and looks right. If the waterlines, diagonals, and buttocks check, she will be spot on.

All that remains to be drawn in now is the keel shape and crown of the deck. Your keel shape can be drawn right on the center line while you can use a clear floor area to establish the deck crown.

While the loft drawing is still clean, it is a good idea to make up a pattern in plywood or cardboard of the rudder shape. This can be put to one side for later use.

If you are satisfied that everything is exactly as should be, actual construction now begins. And right away that means pipe-bending.

Pipe-Bending:

This may sound like a tricky operation—but really it isn't. By the time you have bent your first half-dozen you will be quite an expert in the field!

But, first of all you must start off with the right material. The type of pipe you use is half-inch *inside* diameter black water pipe available at any reputable plumbing supply store in 20-foot lengths. A pipe-cutter is used for cutting the pipe to the lengths required and this can usually be rented or obtained cheaply second-hand.

To bend the pipe it is advisable to use a pipe-bender, electrician's hickey or something similar. You are attempting to bend the pipe without kinking so you must use something which has a curved groove for the size of pipe being used. Under no circumstances should you attempt to bend the pipe in an ordinary vice or anything with a hard corner. That way you could not avoid putting a kink in it.

It should also be realized that this pipe framework is not used to give any structural strength to your boat. It is simply there to give you the shape.

You should set up your pipe-bender close to your floor loft because you will be making frequent checks on the curves as you go along.

The pipe is first cut approximately one foot longer than the station requires and you must bend two identical shapes for each station—one for each side.

To start the actual bending of the pipe, first drive 2″ finishing nails along the length of your loft line—*exactly on the line*. The pipe is bent on the *inside* of these nails. Start bending from one end, not the middle. This allows you to correct as you go along. If you try correcting bends from the middle you'll find that both your ends go out.

You can mark the pipe with a plumbers' grease pencil to show you where the bend is due. After practice, you should be able to bend one pipe in approximately an hour. Don't get discouraged if your first attempt finishes up beneath the boat shed looking like a corkscrew.

Once your pipes (one for each side) are bent to the correct shapes you have to mark on your sheer line, the load water-line and cut off the bottom at the keel, allowing for the thickness of the keel pipe. These marks are best cut in with a hacksaw so that they can be easily found later on.

As you complete your pairs of stations, store them together neatly marked. This is important as stations in the centre of the boat vary only very slightly and if you're not careful you can wind up with a jigsaw puzzle.

A 36-foot ketch begins to take shape in Japan. First the pipe framework traces the outline of the hull.

Now in careful order bend up the stem pipe allowing it to run wild beyond the overhead baseline; the pipe for each side of the keel; the stern post pipe and the transom.

Going to your deck beam loft, bend up a beam for each station, carefully measuring out the length required. Be sure to mark in the centerline on these beams and then cut off to the correct lengths, not forgetting to allow for pipe thickness at each end.

You are now approaching the stage where you set up the pipe framework. This is done by working from an overhead horizontal baseline. To make this baseline, weld together, one to the end of the other, two lengths of pipe which you must fasten rigidly, level and straight beneath the roof of your shed. This overhead line must be directly above the centerline of the loft. The shape and size of your shed roof will dictate how you fasten this piping securely—but it must be secure, perfectly horizontal and plumbed to the centerline. Before fixing, however, cut in marks to correspond with station, stem and transom positions on the floor loft. This is best done by laying the pipe directly on the floor loft, using the top baseline.

Once the overhead baseline is securely in position beneath the roof you can assemble your stations. The two halves are put back on the loft for a final check and the deck beam put in place.

It is important to remember that a number of these stations will be attached to the keel and a short spacer is needed to hold them apart at the bottom. The stations which merely join the stem or stern pipes can be welded together to form a triangle. The length of spacers required for the keel stations is obviously governed by the width of the keel at the joining position.

Spacers and deck beams are simply tack-welded together. This is to assist you later should any of the joints have to be changed.

While the station is still lying on the loft it is a good idea to cut your vertical supporting pipe. This is the pipe which holds the station in place while assembling. It runs from the keel right past your overhead baseline in the roof. It is, of course, tack welded in place so that the bottom is square to the bottom of the keel. Be sure that this vertical pipe touches your deck beam mark and overhead base-

With the hull shape obtained, the horizontal reinforcing rods are fastened in place.

Where the rods overlap, tie securely.

line mark with the edge of the pipe only. This means the pipe is slightly offset but the edge gives you true center.

Do not yet trim any of the station pipes which extend above the deck beam. These are later faired off, using a batten.

All the stations can now be assembled, suspended from the overhead baseline and tack welded in place. The stem pipe is then arc welded into place, followed by the keel, stern-pipe and transom. This leaves your boat literally hanging in the air.

Next step is to shore up the keel to support the boat throughout construction. But before shoring, you must apply your chicken wire under the keel, allowing the edges to overlap so they can be joined up later. This chicken wire, four layers of half-inch 22-gauge, is applied to the outside of the keel bottom and can be twitched on with tie-wire if required.

A two-inch plank is now run along the keel bottom for its full width and well blocked to the floor. It is also a good idea to add braces to avoid any movement of keel and boat during construction.

Fairing:

This is done to ensure that the lines of your boat are true. If you have been careful up to now, fairing should be an easy job.

Again we use battens along the length of the boat to check the fairness. Three battens are run down each side, one at the top, one at the turn of the bilge and one approximately at the water line. Any stations which don't line up properly are now adjusted into a correct position. This is why you have only tack-welded things together. Simply break your joint and correct where necessary. Don't forget the batten is the boss. *Make your boat fit the batten—not vice versa!* When everything is perfect, and only when everything is perfect, weld everything *solid.*

Now is a good time to transfer your load water-line level across to the side of your shed. This is a sly and useful trick which takes the guesswork out of establishing a true water-line after you have applied mortar. You don't need to tell anyone you have done this — just tell everyone that when your boat is launched you're confident you'll have hit the water-line right.

The next move is to fair-up your deck level, trimming off the excess pipe on the stations. But, before doing this it is best to tie on a horizontal bar, the full length of the boat to prevent undue movement.

To fair up the deck you can use a 2x4 to make sure of the fair sheer. Deck beams can be adjusted if required at this stage. Note that the deck beams for cabin and cockpit are cut in later.

Springing a batten around the sheer, the pipe station ends can now be trimmed off flush with the deck.

The importance of this fairing cannot be over-emphasized. Anything out of line at this point will produce a hump or hollow in the boat when it is plastered.

Rods:

You have now reached the stage where hard drawn wire reinforcing rods are attached. These are spaced closer on the longitudinal than on the vertical—see plans. Where they join, overlap joints about one foot and tie securely.

The rods are best tied in place with construction type wire. Welding will tend to distort their shape. The ends where they join stem and stern are hooked around the pipe and well secured. Welding can be done here if required.

You will probably find that amidships you require extra rods to take in the fullness and maintain the 2″ spacing. These 'cheater' rods are simply faired in where they meet the full-length horizontals.

Now your hull is really beginning to take shape and before you move to the next stage the toe-rail should be put in place. For this you use lengths of rod, approximately 12-inches long. These are tied in vertically along the inside of the sheer, extending about five inches above the deck beam. These should be approximately six inches apart. A batten is then lashed horizontally across these to the desired height. A bolt-cutter, laid on top of the batten, will snip off all the excess ends.

The deck is the next step. Here, the horizontal bars, still two inches apart, follow the outside curve of the deck. At the stem and stern they will obviously overlap. This is desirable for added strength and where the bars cross they are tied with wire. When doing the deck, however, do not forget to leave the spaces for cockpit and cabin. And, another important point— do not use any bent or kinked rods for this job. Nor should you put any undue weight on these rods at this stage. You might think you can straighten them out but when wet mortar is applied later you'll soon realize you didn't do an effective job.

For this task of applying the deck rods it is best to rig up some form of scaffold inside the structure.

Application of the chicken wire — a tedious chore.

Also remember a weight factor is now coming into the construction picture and it is a good time to fasten the corner of each deck beam to the rafters of your shed with good strong wire. Several strands of wire will do this job. Insert a stick between the wires so that you can twist them tight. They will take the load of the boat as you progress.

Provision should now be made for the propellor and shaft log. Pipe must be bent as shown on the plan to make up the shape of the aperture in which the prop. turns. The shaft log is also welded in now as detailed on the plan.

Chainplates and other rigging fittings as specified in the plans can also be fitted at this stage if required. Some builders will prefer to weld them into the structure at this stage while others may prefer to bolt them in place after the hull is complete. There are arguments for and against each method. One is liable to produce a leak while the other can create problems if there is any failure in the fitting. If you're going to weld, however, now's the time to do it.

Chicken Wire Mesh:

Application of the chicken wire is the next job— and if you're at the end of your patience, go away somewhere for a quiet weekend before you start this phase of the job. We make no bones about it—this is a tedious job. And, you might even have a headache before you start the job—that is, you may have to hunt around to find the correct 22-gauge, half-inch mesh that is essential. It is readily available in Canada but in some parts of the U.S. and the rest of the world it is apparently quite hard to come by. Its sole use up to now appears to have been confined to the construction of budgie cages. With eight layers overall, you're going to need quite a lot of the stuff so don't be surprised if the storekeeper thinks you're breeding budgies by the million.

The mesh is made only in Japan, West Germany and Belgium and it is advisable to have placed an order well in advance. The handiest size is the 36-inch wide rolls which come in lengths of 150 feet. You could check with foreign trade consuls regarding manufacturers and their agents in your country.

There are also two different kinds of mesh. One type is galvanized in production and the other hot-dipped later. Experience has shown the latter type to be superior, it being stiffer and less prone to sagging when the wet mortar is applied. Again, however, you

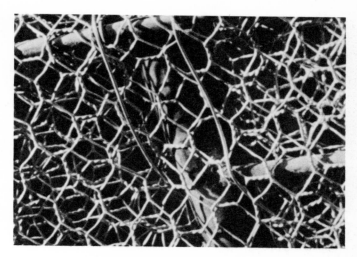

The mesh must be laced tightly.

may have to make do with whatever type you can purchase in your area.

Once you have bought the mesh the hard work begins. If you have managed to get 150-foot lengths, 36 inches wide, they should be opened out to the full length of the section you are working on from sheer to keel, and then doubled over to 18-inch width along this full length.

Measurements are taken from the deck to keel, following the curve. These lengths of doubled wire are then 'hung' from the deck line along the length of the boat, edge to edge. This obviously gives you a two layer mesh. The operation is then repeated with the next double layer overlapping your first double layer joints. Now she's four layers thick as required. The mesh can now be attached to the piping and bars at various points and really tightened. The same operation is repeated on the inside and now you have eight layers.

Again a warning. Keep this mesh good and tight. There should be no loose ends or stray cut pieces, no sags, bumps, or hollows.

At the keel you can now join up the overlapping pieces from the mesh on the keel bottom. At the stem and stern the mesh can be lapped round, tucking in any sharp edges of the mesh.

And now, tedium. The lengthy process of lacing the mesh all over the framework begins and this is the trying part of cement-boat construction. Many mechanical methods of lashing the mesh to the frame have been attempted but so far nothing has been found to beat tieing the wire by hand. If anyone comes up with a faster method he will stand first in line as patron saint of cement boat builders.

The mesh should be laced vertically, starting from the deck level down to the keel at about four-inch intervals.

It is ideal to have one man on the inside, one out, using long tie wires in a stitching pattern. The aim is to cinch the mesh as close to the bars as possible, taking care not to draw the mesh in between the rods. You should achieve a half-inch sandwich of mesh and rod which is as smooth on the inside as it is out. There should be no corrugation whatsoever. Again, the individual builder will probably evolve his own 'stitching' method to suit himself. When anyone comes up with a practical time-saving idea, we'll be pleased to hear about it and will pass it on to other builders.

Odds and Ends:

You are now getting close to the exciting part of your cement-boat project—the plastering. But, before you prepare for this big day there are a number of odds and ends to take care of. Now is the time to make provision for bulkheads, floors, skin-fittings, gudgeons, fuel tanks, watertight bulkheads, scuppers and any other hull attachments you may require.

Bulkheads are made up from ¾-inch plywood or two ⅜-inch plywood laminates and are attached to the webs shown on the S.M.D.E. plan. These webs seldom fall on stations, so the easiest way to ensure that they are installed vertically is to go back to the loft and make up stations from the loft where the webs go. They can be made smaller all around to be sure they are easily fitted into the hull. After these rough lumber stations have been fastened in place, bend ¼-inch reinforcing bar at approximately right angles so that one end lays flat alongside the station while the other is inserted between the mesh and lies parallel with a longitudinal rod. These rods are required at about 6-inch centers. They should protrude into the hull for about a foot. They are later trimmed off and capped with a 1-inch strap screed. Wire is then attached along either side.

Remember that the bulkheads are the backbone of your joinery work. They establish the lines for your bunks, cupboards, and other interior woodwork, so *they must be square and plumb to the waterline.* If you get off on the wrong foot here you'll wind up sleeping in a sloping bunk—and that isn't much fun.

Plastering day — with pozzolan, Type V cement and sand all ready to hand.

Even youngsters can help by screening the sand.

Floor supports go in next, as detailed on the plans. These are made up from short lengths of rod placed across the bilge and tied or welded. It is a good idea to 'turn' the ends of these rods at right-angles for about nine inches to facilitate fastening. These form extensions of the webs on the side of the hull.

You must now also blank out your limber holes at the top of the ballast and attach your engine beds as shown on the plan. (The limber holes prevent water being trapped at any intervals along the length of the boat, facilitating gathering for discharge by pumping.)

Skin fittings go in next and it is advisable here to use the nylon variety which are corrosion free. These fittings are required for the head, sink, self-bailing cockpit, drains, salt-water galley pump and maybe for a water-cooled engine. Having obtained the fittings you should make up "blanks" from three-quarter inch plywood. These "blanks" are made to the exact diameter of the fittings and inserted into the hull at the desired spots before plastering. When the hull is complete you can simply punch out this plywood and insert the fitting itself. If you have any portholes in the side of the hull, they are treated in the same way, using blanks until the hull is complete.

Obviously some care is needed in making up the blanks—they must be the exact size or else you will wind up with a slack fitting or one that can't even be forced into place.

Moving down to the stern of the boat you also now attach the gudgeons and the rudder tube as shown on the plan.

If you are constructing a work-boat, this is also the time to put in fuel tanks, water-tight bulkheads, etc. These may be made up in the ferro-cement but allowance must be made for baffles, inspection plates, drain and filler holes in the fuel tanks. Fuel and water filler holes should also be blanked out on the deck in the same way that the skinfittings are done.

You can now turn your attention to the deck and make provision for cabin and cockpit. This simply means cutting away the deck beams where they cross the cabin and cockpit areas. But first, think of more support. Where you cut out the middle portion of the beam you will need overhead bracing to prevent the deck sagging. Simply get scrap ends of rods and spot weld them to the boat framework wherever possible and attach them to the rafters or other overhead supports. They can be broken out of the deck after

The result of the screening—a good texture sand with the correct mixture of coarse and fine particles. This sand has passed a No. 8 sieve.

Screened out of the ordinary mortar sand are these larger particles. If left in, they would bind up in the mesh and hinder penetration.

61

Into the mixer goes a carefully measured amount of water.

. . . and into the mixer, after the cement, pozzolan and water, goes the sand.

Now the mortar is mixed and dumped out onto a special holding tray.

A quick check to test that the texture of the mortar is correct.

The application of the mortar—forced first into difficult corners.

In some areas, forcing by hand is advisable.

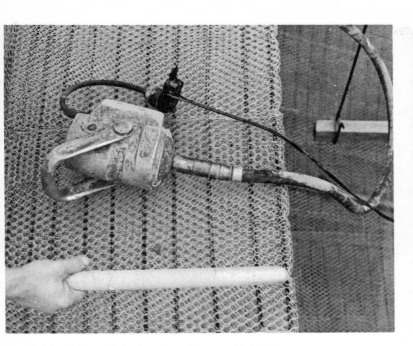

A valuable aid on plastering day—the pencil vibrator.

Working along the frame, the pencil vibrator ensures good penetration.

From the outside the vibrator can be seen to have done its job well. Good penetration has been achieved.

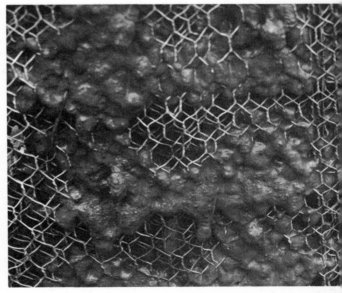

Mortar has been forced through from the inside. The plastering will now be completed from the outside.

A 41-foot Orams designed cutter stands ready for plastering day.

Braced on all sides, the hull is set to take the weight of the wet mortar.

the mortar has gone hard and the spots filled with epoxy and cement.

You should also note that these supporting rods are left in throughout the plastering stage and are cut off and sealed only in the very final stages.

If you cut them away too soon you'll be in real danger of seeing your boat sag when the wet mortar is applied. Don't forget you are going to apply several tons of cement, so be sure the bracing is good and tight. Take time out to check this now. You should have this bracing all along the edge of the boat at about two foot intervals together with the bracing from the cockpit and cabin edges.

You are now getting closer to the actual plastering —but one more job must be done. The edges of the cabin and cockpit must be 'capped' with one-eighth-inch mild galvanized steel. This steel strapping, of about 1½ inches width, is welded in place on edge, covering the open ends of the deck beam piping and allowing for the extra thickness of cement when applied. This capping also serves as a useful guide for the plasterer to work to when smoothing off the deck. This capping remains in place when the plastering is complete and is later epoxied to prevent corrosion.

The same capping is now also applied to the toe rail only this time you only need one-inch wide strapping. Again, however, take some care. This capping gives you the final line on your sheer, so there should be absolutely no kinking or bending in the steel. And again, it is advisable to use a wooden batten first to get your correct line. A neat job here helps give your finished boat a neat, clean profile line.

Where the bends are not severe it may be advisable to use a 'T' strap. This makes attachment of the rods to the screeds much easier.

Put in your scuppers now—and at last you are ready for that big job.

Plastering:

Take a deep breath—or a weekend off, whichever you prefer—and away we go. First the preparations. You *must* build a scaffold. This can be built up any way that you want but it must give you access to every corner of the boat without actually putting any weight on the hull itself. Ideally it should not touch the boat anywhere — contact would cause undue shaking and movement. You should not have to walk or put any weight on any section of the mesh framework to

Plastering day—but under rainy conditions.

At the end of the tiring day owner Chas. Strange of New Zealand and his helpers take a well-earned rest.

do the plastering. Again, ideally, the scaffold should go completely around the boat. On plastering day you will have enough to do without the additional trouble and delay of moving a clumsy scaffold around as you progress.

On the big plastering day itself, all materials must be on the site well in advance. You are going to plaster the whole boat in one day — it is certainly not advisable to break this job down. This, of course, means that you want everything to hand and you also need many hands to help you — up to six to ten friends. You might find it well worth while to employ a professional man whose skill in trowelling will help you get that perfect finish on your boat.

It is also a good idea to order more cement and sand than you will need. If you run short of material you are in for trouble. The betting is that if you run short it will be in the evening when all the supply sources are closed and that means real problems. So, get more material than you need—you can always use it in the ballast.

The materials you will need for the plastering are sand, cement, pozzolan, and epoxy.

The sand should be of a sharp fine grade, and, of course, dry. This is the usual mortar sand and it pays you to get the best quality. The sand gives you the strength in your cement mix so there is no point in skimping in this area. Get the best you can — at most it will only cost you a few dollars more. The better the sand, the stronger the mix and the longer the life of your boat.

Sand is the key to the watertightness and impermeability of ferro-cement. Be careful to have it graded. If it cannot be obtained in the proper grades, batch the sand yourself. Note, all sand should pass a No. 8 sieve — 10 - 15 per cent fines should pass a No. 100 sieve. The grading curve should be quite even for the in-between sizes. Do not have a lot of particles the same size. They should vary so they will interlock to form a dense, watertight shell. Try to obtain sand originating from crushed rock of an igneous nature. Make inquiries at your local cement contractor's and talk over aggregates with him. He will be able to advise you as to which is the best type of sand produced locally and you will need his assurance that your sand will pass the sieve test requirements as above detailed.

Type of cement is a pure matter of choice. We

First the cement is applied from the inside.

The job is completed from the outside.

The plasterer must ensure that there is good penetration.

The final skim coat should just cover the mesh.

have successfully used Type 5 Portland which is an alkali resistant. Some builders prefer to use a high-early cement which gives them a hull which can be trowelled smooth quickly. But, what they gain in curing time they may lose in time for careful application. It's a matter of preference.

It should be remembered that cement is only a type of glue which is holding the sand. A mixture of two parts of sand to one of cement is about as rich as you should go. Anything richer than this would only reduce strength. The pozzolan clay is added at a ratio of 15 pounds per sack of cement. The pozzolan is added as an aid to salt water resistance. The mortar used in ferro-cement should be very dense. Pozzolan adds the right kind of fines to bring about this densification.

Water, of course, must be added to make the whole deal work. The amount will vary according to the amount of water content in the sand.

Often too little attention is paid to the water ratio but this is the key to the whole mix. It is the water that triggers the curing action. But, excess water leaves the cement by evaporation and there is then a tendency for hair-line cracks to appear on the surface. This is avoided by not using too much water—but just the right amount. Too watery a mix also tends to 'leech' the cement out to the surface of the mix under trowelling, again resulting in weakening. With too much water the mix also becomes too heavy and loses some of its adhering quality on the horizontal planes of the boat. Approximately 4¼ gallons per bag is a good guide.

So, aim for a stiff but workable mix and don't splash that water around with gay abandon when you are batching. And some other do's and don'ts of the mixing business.

1. Don't attempt to rejuvenate cement left over from a mix which has started to set and harden. Make up a fresh batch and start again.

2. Do mix your cement thoroughly.

3. Don't keep on mixing forever while you are working. When mixed thoroughly dump out and use as quickly as needed.

4. Do use clean water at all times.

5. Don't forget to wash all tools and appliances carefully if you take a lunch or coffee break.

How to mix the cement? **You should use a plasterers' mixer in which the paddle wheels revolve horizontally.**

An ordinary mixer will not give you a dry enough mix.

First put in your water and allow this to swirl around for a minute or so. Now add the pozzolan. This is best sieved in so no lumps develop. It must all dissolve. If pozzolan is allowed to remain lumpy it will never 'cure' in the mix. Soft lumps will remain, with obviously detrimental results.

Next comes the cement followed by the sand. Most plasterers mixers will take two bags of cement and four bags of sand. If you have employed a professional plasterer for the job, he, of course, will be able to advise on this mixing procedure.

All you have to do now is put your 'instant skin' on your boat. And this is the equipment you should have at hand for the job. A good long length of garden hose is essential for washing down and general cleaning of tools, etc. A good number of metal buckets are needed for carrying mix and water. Plasterers' trowels, hocks, pencil vibrator, and flexible screeds are required for the actual application. You could also have on hand some hot rum to lubricate the mix operators. Generally known as Nelson's blood, this liquid has proved invaluable in a number of operations. What Nelson himself would think of its use in the construction of a cement boat is open to question!

If you are working without a plasterer, it will be a good idea before you tackle this big day to have done some experimenting with the mix. Make up a couple of sample panels and get the feel of the medium. It really will help.

One other important step that must be undertaken before you begin any plastering is to ensure that oxydization of the mesh and framework is complete. This is achieved as you work on wire-tieing by regular wetting of the framework and mesh for some two or three weeks before your big day. This will remove any mill-scale, grease or glossiness on the metal and give a better bond with the mix. You might see your precious framework going a little rusty in spots — but don't worry. That's just ideal and helps the bond.

Also a coat of epoxy should previously have been applied to all the metal surfaces which will be left bare after the cement is applied, i.e. toe-rail, gudgeons, chain plates, cabin and cockpit cappings, etc. On plastering day itself you can put on a second epoxy coat which will help bonding in those areas if the mix is applied while the epoxy is still wet.

For a heavy displacement hull, a strong scaffold.

Careful attention is first paid to the difficult areas.

Now, at last, you are ready to plaster! Get up very early and get lots and lots of dedicated and enthusiastic helpers—as well as your professional man. The help will shovel, carry, wheel, dump and fill. They'll make sure when the plastering hands yell "more mud!" the stuff will be available.

You should have had plenty of sleep the night before—it's going to be one of the longest and most arduous days of your life!

Basically, the mortar is *always* applied from the *inside* and smoothed down on the outside of the hull. This varies slightly on deck. The deck is plastered in two operations. A thin skin coat of mortar is applied to the underside of the deck on plastering day. This skin coat is allowed to harden for two weeks and thus forms a mold. When this skin has become sufficiently hard, the balance of the deck is applied from the top. Mix a latex bonding agent in with the second application of mortar. This will ensure a good bond.

Note: it is very difficult to plaster the deck all at once for several reasons. The deck is a large flat surface which is nearly horizontal. It is difficult to get mortar to cling to horizontal surfaces such as this, also the weight of the mortar and water is quite great. It is difficult to stop the deck from sagging in places when this great weight is applied. By creating an initial form first you are only putting a portion of this weight in place at one time and so the chance of sagging is minimized. After this under-skin has set it will support the balance of the weight with no difficulty. The required thickness will be less and the finish better.

The deck is tackled first, together with all the awkward corners—those you can't reach without being some kind of a contortionist. It's tough work, but you have to get that cement into all those awkward spots and in many you will have to force it through, using a gloved hand. If you can get your pencil vibrator in on the frames it will assist you in assuring good penetration. Work right around the boat next and cement down all the vertical pipe frames. On the inside of the boat, when the job is complete, you will have slight bulges where these pipe frames protrude. This is normal. You can get a perfectly smooth finish on the outside but unless you are going to build up a tremendous thickness inside you won't get it perfectly flat. And the last thing you want is a thick shell.

Now you can fill in all your between-frame areas all

over the boat with one man forcing the mix through from the inside as another on the outside smoothes it down. The mix is always forced through by hand and carefully worked in, making sure there are no air-pockets. All it requires is practice—and this day you'll get plenty of it.

Finish off the keel to the same general thickness of the rest of the boat but inside the surface of the plaster can be whisked with a stiff broom. This will form a good key for the ballast to adhere to when added later.

As the mix begins to cure around the boat, your professional man should come into his own. He is the man to put the trowel finish on the outside and in the long run, this will decide the finished appearance of your boat. Any mark will show so, if you have hired help, get a good man who really knows his job. In fact, it might be advisable to have a second professional man on hand for this latter stage of the job. It is likely that it will be reaching evening before you get to this smoothing down and by then you will have a few tired men around.

A fresh man coming into the job at this stage could make all the difference. This really is the vital time and in a couple of hours you can make or mar your boat. It will be advisable to make sure you have adequate lighting available at this time. If it is going dark you could easily miss a bad spot in the shadows. It's too late if you see it the morning after!

To finish the outside of the skin, use a sponge trowel. Go all over the shell in a circular motion, this will leave a sandy surface but it is much preferable to a streaky surface left by a trowel. DO NOT allow the mortar to build up over ⅛-inch over the outside wire. If you get excessive building up you will find you have added many hundreds of pounds to your boat, but no extra strength. The mortar is only strong in conjunction with steel. Also, when a rich mix like this is applied and allowed to build-up where there is no steel to strengthen it, hair line cracking may occur. This will not normally be serious as the cracks seldom go below the wire but just the same they are to be avoided. They could retain water.

Now, however, the big job is done. Just keep away from the boat until the cement is really dry. Don't shake the freshly plastered hull or vibrate it—if you do you're liable to undo your own good work. In fact, just all go home to bed and get your well deserved rest—there's more work ahead the next day. This is when you start sanding with the carborundum

Work begins on achieving the finish.

At last the work is done, the hull complete.

stone and carborundum sandpaper. Your cement is still a long way off its final hard cure and this is the time to work hard for the finish. As soon as you've got her sanded down to your complete satisfaction begin the wetting down process. For two or three weeks from the cementing day your boat must be kept continually wet—both inside and out. It might even be a good idea to set up a makeshift sprinkler system to achieve this more readily.

There are several types of carborundum stones. Use the coarse cement finishers first, then do your fine sanding with a tool sharpening stone. After the hull is rubbed down well, any little deformities may be filled using a fiberglass filler such as used on auto-body work. This should be done after the hull has been etched and before the epoxy has been applied. This filler can produce a very slick surface if sanded with wet or dry sandpaper. Try to get a good finish with the stones and do not revert to gallons of filler as this shoots the cost up and is not the workmanlike way to do it.

You can punch a good drainhole in the bottom of the keel to let the water drain away from inside and this hole can easily be filled later.

Keep off the boat during this three-week wetting down period and avoid uneven curing by keeping the wind away from her. Nor should you be doing this plastering and curing process in freezing weather.

That's asking for more trouble.

The reason you are keeping the cement wetted down for such a long period is to effect a good cure. As soon as cement dries it stops curing.

When the curing process is complete you can immediately start to "smarten" up your boat. First you give her a muriatic acid wash. Dilute the acid with plenty of water and then neutralize this with a wash of diluted caustic soda. This will give you the key for all paints, etc. Take your hose and swill the boat down thoroughly after these washes.

A couple of coats of thycol based epoxy inside and out are desirable to really seal the shell—although she is good and watertight as she is. Sand down this epoxy and give her a good quality undercoat.

Now we go back to our underhand trick — transferring the waterline back from the side of the shed, using a batten to make it a good fair curve all round. Paint on your boot-top, anti-fouling on the bottom and a good white paint on top.

The boat is now looking smart and trim and you can invite your friends around to look her over. In fact, if you have to, you can now launch her and prepare to do your woodwork and other finishing afloat.

The boat is now looking smart and trim and you can invite your friends over to look at her.

This small sailing sloop was built in Vancouver, Canada, by co-author John Samson, Hank Dirksen, Hank Vandenburg, Reg Clark and Jim Kreeft.

CHAPTER 10

THE CEDAR MOLD METHOD

We now turn to the alternative method of ferro-cement boat construction—the cedar mold technique. This is a method specially developed by Samson Marine Design Enterprises Ltd. in a bid to speed up the building time and give a better finished boat.

In short, the cedar mold method will give a boat which is fairer in line in far less time than by using the pipe framework system.

It should, however, be clearly understood that while the pipe framework method is well proven through trial and error, the cedar mold technique is still in its infancy. It has not been time-tested.

Several hulls have been completed using molds and they have shown conclusively that the time saved in construction is impressive.

One obvious advantage of the mold technique is that by building the hull upside down you are working on a solid base. This eliminates any chance of the framework sagging as the work progresses.

As the name suggests, the cedar mold method sees the ferro-cement boat made with the assistance of temporary wooden molds or station frames on which the whole form will be shaped and built. We recommend cedar as the ideal wood for the shell—but any soft wood can be used.

In effect, you build a very inexpensive wooden boat to which you will be molding your ferro-cement.

Time consuming lashing of chicken wire is eliminated as this mesh, together with the rod, is simply nailed or stapled onto the wooden structure.

Water pipe is not used at all in this method of construction, but this does not detract in any way from the strength of the finished hull. In the original building method, the pipe is used merely to create form and shape and, to provide a base to which can be attached the mesh and rod. It does, of course, further form a rigid frame which helps support the wet mortar. With the cedar mold technique, this role is assumed by the wooden framework.

But now let us take the cedar mold technique step by step. First, the molds must be made up for the stations and for areas where webs are called for on the plans. Ideally, these are made up from 1x12 spruce shelving or some other easy-to-work wood which is reasonably inexpensive.

A pick-up board is made up as shown in S.M.D.E. plans. This is used to pick up the lines from the loft floor and transfer them to the wood to be cut into station molds.

Do not forget that when taking measurements from your loft for these frames you must subtract one and one-half inches from the outside of the shell as shown on the plans. This is to allow for the combined thickness of the wood and the ferro-cement. The out-

side measurement of your completed boat must conform exactly to the measurements shown in the plans.

A strongback must also be constructed at this stage. When the station molds are all assembled they will be fastened securely to this.

To make up the station molds, the pick-up board is laid over the area of the loft where the sections are drawn. Each strip on the pick-up board is ticked where it intersects with a section. This is the easiest method of transferring the lines on the loft floor to a board. The outline is indicated on the pick-up board and now, using the 1x2 spruce lumber, the station molds can be cut to their correct shape.

A powered hand saw can be used to cut out the easier curves but where these become more severe it may be found necessary to remove small pieces of lumber at a time. A band saw would, of course, simplify this cutting tremendously.

After the station molds are carefully joined together, they are marked and set aside.

The next step is to make up the keel and this is best achieved by laying narrow strips of 1x2 together on their flat plane. A piece of plywood is scabbed to the top of the keel which will remain inside the boat when plastering is completed. This is done to facilitate stripping out of the 1x2 lumber later. If the keel was laid in one solid piece, it would be nearly impossible to remove without damaging the bottom of the hull.

The stem and transom are now made up. And it is time to turn back to the strongback. To build this rigid structure, long 2x12 boards are nailed together with the joints overlapping until you have fabricated two straight lengths of timber 4x12 and extending two feet longer than the boat to be built.

Now 2x4 braces are laid across the long straight rails and nailed firmly in position. These are nailed

On the loft floor—a sailboat begins to take shape.

on the edge of the station marks which are taken off the plan. Snap a center line down the middle of the braces as was done when lofting. Line up the center of the station molds to this, nailing them firmly in place. Care should be taken to ensure they are at 90 degrees to the base. A few temporary battens sprung along the length of the boat will help secure them in place until they are firmly positioned.

The keel is then put in place, the stem notched in and the transom set. Another batten is now sprung along the framework to check for fairness — and remember, the batten is still the boss. The frames must fit the batten not vice versa. To fair up any of these molds they can be shaved with a plane or packed up with thin strip lumber.

Now, planking must be applied overall, starting at the sheer line. But first, measure the height of the toe rail, using a "starting board" which is at least 2 inches wider than the specified rail. The bottom of this board should come level with the *top* of the deck line. You will strike your sheer on this board. This is done by using a lofting batten and drawing in a very fair and very accurate sheer line. Above this line (or below as you are now working upside down) is attached a three-quarter-inch thick strip which will act as a screed when plastering.

Now a 1½-inch spacer must be placed at each station. These spacers are fitted snugly against the starting board. These spacers will create a gap into which mesh and rod are later turned to form a lap which joins with the deck reinforcing.

Now the inexpensive sheathing of the hull with the nominal 1x4 dressed cedar lumber (or other easy to work soft wood) can begin. This is done working upwards from the spacers. The strips should be nailed together as neatly as possible with the edges meeting.

A light batten is used to spring in the curves.

A line of nails traces the outline of a station.

All ready for the mold building method, the station frames are stacked in order.

A firm strongback is laid down the centre of the shed.

Firmly in place the frames reach high into the shed roof.

All in place the frames are further secured by a horizontal batten.

The first frames are secured in position on the strongback.

The frames are nailed firmly to the rails of the strongback.

The planking begins. Note gap left for turning in rods and mesh to form deck.

From inside the hull—the planking is fairing-in good and true.

Above left: The transom calls for special attention. Carefully cut sections provide the shape.

Above: Narrow planks are nailed in position vertically.

Left: Finally planked and ready to be trimmed to shape.

At the stem, carefully cut sections also provide fullness and shape. The sections are notched home.

Running from the stem-head down the keel, thin wooden laths form the curved mold.

Slight gaps will not, however, create too serious a problem as this wooden lining is later stripped out from the inside of the finished hull.

When the curves become too difficult to meet and fit, switch to sheathing from the keel downwards. It is unlikely that you will have planks long enough to run the whole length of the boat, so these must be joined neatly along their length. To do this, butt blocks are attached at the joints on the inside. These can be made up from scrap plywood or other lumber. The joints must be perfectly fair on the outside.

Towards the stern, the sheathing may start to tend to shingle or overlap as some of the curves are quite severe. To achieve neat planking in these areas, the planks can be ripped in half using a hand power saw and will prove much easier to handle and fit.

When the whole mold is planked it should be planed to ensure perfect fairness.

Now a vapor barrier is applied all over. Plastic or tar paper is perfect for this. The barrier will prevent excess mortar running between cracks and joints when the hull is plastered and will give a smooth finish on the inside of the boat when the wood is eventually stripped out.

Next step is to apply the chicken wire netting. The ends of the chicken wire mesh are stuffed through the gap left at the starting board. At least one foot of mesh should be pushed into the gap.

Four layers of the mesh are applied as tightly as you can possibly manage, fastening it to the wooden mold with staples or short clinched nails. Four further layers are now pushed into the gap but these are left hanging down on the floor. They will be fastened into position after the horizontal and vertical rods are attached. They are inserted through the gap at this stage for reasons which will be obvious when the

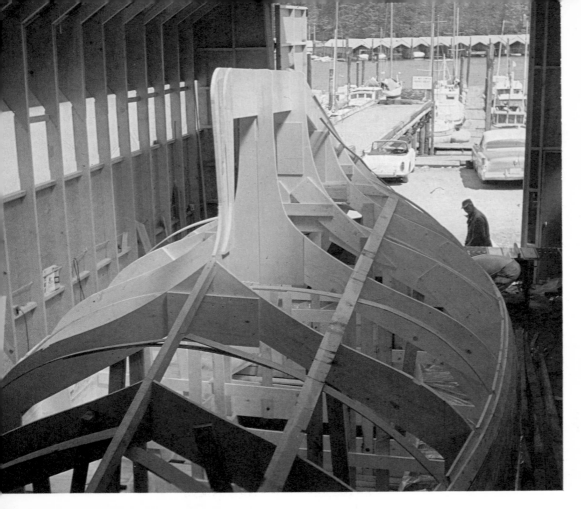

Birds-eye-view as the mold begins to grow. Batten still used to hold frames steady.

Now the batten is gone as the planking reaches up into the keel area.

The wooden mold is complete and it is time to apply the mesh. First comes a plastic vapor barrier and then the mesh is forced into the gap left at the deck level.

The loose mesh is neatly trimmed off with shears.

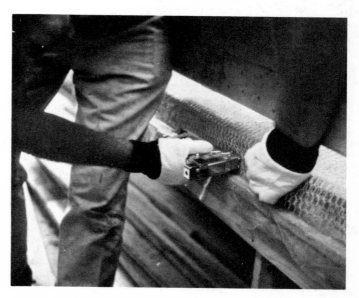

The mesh is then firmly stapled into place. This is just one of the four layers.

vertical rods are applied. These rods carry over the gap and it would be nearly impossible to get the mesh into place in the gap after they are in place.

Two different kinds of rod are used in the next phase. A lighter rod is used for the vertical and heavier for horizontal as specified in S.M.D.E. plans, according to the hull. The light vertical rods go on first and are stapled in place at six-inch centers. As earlier indicated, these carry across the gap at the starting board. Short rods must also be cut at this stage and bent at right angles. These are also stapled to the wooden form with the end protruding through the gap in readiness to form the lap joint with the deck. Sufficient of these should be made up to be placed at 2-inch centers and where they abut an existing vertical they should be firmly lashed. It should be borne in mind that these shorter rods must have

Above left: Layers of pre-folded mesh at a station point will later turn into the hull to form webs for the bulkheads.

Above: At the stem, special attention is paid to neatness. The reinforcing rods protruding from the gap will later join hull and deck.

Left: With the four layers of mesh stapled in place the rods are bent into place and also stapled down.

sufficient length to carry across the side decks. These rods are later trimmed off to length after the inside mold has been removed. Also blank off places to prepare for through hull fittings, shaft log, and rudder fittings. These will also be set in place after the hull is finished. Where the shaft log and rudder gland go through, holes must be drilled to a larger size and stuffed with wire and rebar to afford a bond to the fittings which are inserted later. Starter rods should also be left for the engine beds.

Provision must also be made at this stage for the installation of the interior webs. Where these are indicated on the plans, holes should be drilled through the wood from keel to starting board. Through these holes are inserted two foot lengths of right angle rod. On the outside, these rods are laid horizontally along the planking and firmly secured. The horizontal full length rods can now be stapled into place at 6-inch centers.

These horizontals should be well lapped at stem and stern. The top four layers of chicken wire can now be picked up and fastened tightly into place all over the hull.

A quick check can be made with a nail all over the hull to see that thickness is even and as thin as possible overall.

This is an important point to watch. Weight is a problem in ferro-cement construction and if care is not exercised the skin will become too thick and heavy. *Extra thickness does not mean extra strength — only extra weight.*

A boat is a floating object and every additional pound in weight will only serve to push her deeper into the water and impair her performance.

Stapling is quicker than lacing—but still a chore. The mesh must be fastened down securely before the vertical re-inforcing rods can be put in place.

Resembling a giant whale, the 40-foot sailboat is now ready to receive the horizontal reinforcing rods.

A stem view shows the heavier reinforcing rods running down the keel.

In close-up, the three-quarter-inch plywood skin fitting blank clearly indicates the thickness of the hull.

Now we have arrived again at the big plastering day. In this method, the hull should be plastered in three passes. The first pass should be with a rather soft mix. This is to ensure that the mortar will be forced right in through the mesh. The plasterer should be followed by a second man using a vibrator to ensure the mortar fills in behind the rods. The second pass is made at a slightly stiffer mix, with the vibrator again used to ensure penetration.

The final pass is merely to fill in any voids and to smooth out humps and hollows. Again care must be taken not to build up too great a thickness. The wire should be just covered.

The whole hull should be plastered as quickly as possible so that there is no chance of the first pass layer curing before the job is complete.

When the mortar begins to set it should be sponge trowelled until the hull is perfectly smooth all over. A few extra hours of work here while the hull is green save many days of tiring effort when she is cured.

Watering down is started now as in the pipe framework method and when the hull is completely cured it is time to reach for the carborundum stone and begin the finish work. A body filler can be used to patch up the scratches, etc., but if this is necessary the etching process as outlined in the pipe framework method must be completed first.

The end finish result should resemble a china cup. All that remains is to paint on two coats of epoxy, strike the water line as earlier detailed and paint on the anti-fouling.

Painting of the boot top and rest of the hull is also best done at this stage—she looks so much smarter throughout the rest of the construction.

The outside of the boat is now completed but work is going to begin in earnest inside. And that means she must be rolled over. There are many methods of doing this. (See Page 100) Different boats and different terrain may call for varying approaches; but after the boat is turned she must be shored up securely.

Now we start to strip out the interior wooden framing. The tops of the station molds are removed first. These are cut down to three-quarter inches below the deck level, which has been previously marked on the wooden mold. The part of the mold cut away (the strip which lay across the strongback) now serves a secondary purpose. It can be shaped to correspond with the deck crown and is replaced at each station

Here's mud in your eye! A pencil vibrator is worked over the freshly applied plaster, shaking down behind the mesh for perfect penetration. After filling a specially constructed vibrator box with mortar, the steel on the hull is vibrated causing the mixture to flow horizontally.

On the vertical planes the vibrator box and vibrator prove invaluable aids to penetration.

at the height of the underside of the deck. These in effect are now temporary deck beams and the task of setting in the ferro-cement deck can begin. The process of laying inexpensive planking is carried out all over the deck area. Again, the planks must fit exactly and snugly and must be fair all over. The process of adding vapor barrier, mesh and rods is repeated.

Before this is done, however, and to save yourself wasted time and effort, the cabin shape, cockpit, hatches and all deck fillers must be blanked out.

When the rods are applied it must again be remembered to drill holes at the points where webs are placed. Right angle short rods are again inserted through these holes with outside lengths running fore and aft. These inside ends must be parallel because they will form the line of the permanent deck beams.

A good epoxy bonding agent must be used at the point where the deck meets the hull. Stripping out the rest of the interior woodwork is the next step— but this must not be done until the deck has cured,

which will take about three weeks time and the usual wetting of the cement.

A wooden wedge is used to make the stripping job easier. Nails or staples protruding through the concrete must be broken off and the interior ground, using a heavy duty disk grinder.

The surface must next be peened using a welder's hammer. Any pockets of grout or doubtful areas of penetration can be located and cleaned out with a vacuum cleaner.

Mix a latex bonding agent and a thin grout coat to skim the entire inside surface of the hull. The thin grout coat should be made up of one half part of fine sand and one half part of cement. The skim coat will cover the staple ends, etc.

Webs can be done at the same time.

If the initial penetration is good, two coats of epoxy will be sufficient to cover all wire ends.

The bulkheads can now be installed and the boat finished according to plan.

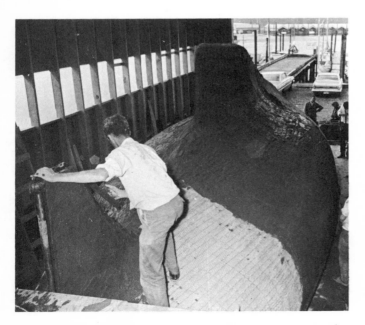

Plastering the cedar mold hull. Here just a small area remains to be covered on the first pass.

The wetting down is complete. Now the hull is ready for etching and the application of an epoxy skin-coat.

CHAPTER 11

WEB FRAMEWORK TECHNIQUE

We refer to our third building method as the web framework technique—a method which should be found to be most suitable for medium-to-large size fishing vessels. Many improvements in ferro-cement building techniques are being made; the web framework method is one example. The refinements it presents would not have been possible without the earlier efforts.

At the outset it must be made clear that the web framework technique is for one-off construction. It was evolved to bring about improvements in structural construction techniques, and not to illustrate production methods. And, while it does streamline construction, the building materials and the end product are the same.

The first consideration is the structure which will support the hull throughout construction—and this can also serve as a shelter. Too much emphasis cannot be placed on this structure and the accompanying drawing details a suitable type of building in which lofting can be carried out under good conditions.

After the lofting is complete, ¾-inch plywood patterns are cut for the webs and bulkheads and on these are carefully marked the waterlines, diagonals and buttocks. This will aid in setting up the hull.

Two layers of ½-inch 22 gauge chicken wire are now lightly stapled to one face of the plywood patterns. The inside edges are neatly trimmed off with shears while the outside edge is allowed to run wild for 6 inches. This overlap will later join into the hull. To achieve this on the curved areas, darts must be cut at 6-inch intervals on the overlap.

While the patterns are still lying on the workshop floor, one-inch by one-eighth-inch strap iron should be attached to the neatly trimmed inside edges and to any edges which will not later mate with mortar. These strap edges will give a neat finish and can be attached in position with nails.

The strap edges are applied where bulwark stanchions, access cut-outs and fish pens occur, together with all areas of framing which are not joined with the hull. These form screeds which give the plasterer a landing for his trowel.

A length of ¼-inch cold-rolled reinforcing bar is now spot welded into the corner formed by the strap edge and the mesh-covered plywood pattern. A second length of ¼-inch reinforcing bar is then stapled to the outside edge of the mesh-covered pattern, giving a true outline of the mold. Continuous lengths of re-bar are then filled in on the pattern on approximately 2-inch centres with shorts welded into areas which form the keel, bulwark braces and engine bed braces.

Short lengths of the ¼-inch reinforcing bar are cut in readiness for positioning across these continuous lengths of rod. They are welded in place on 6-inch centres; odd ones should be attached at 45-deg. angles

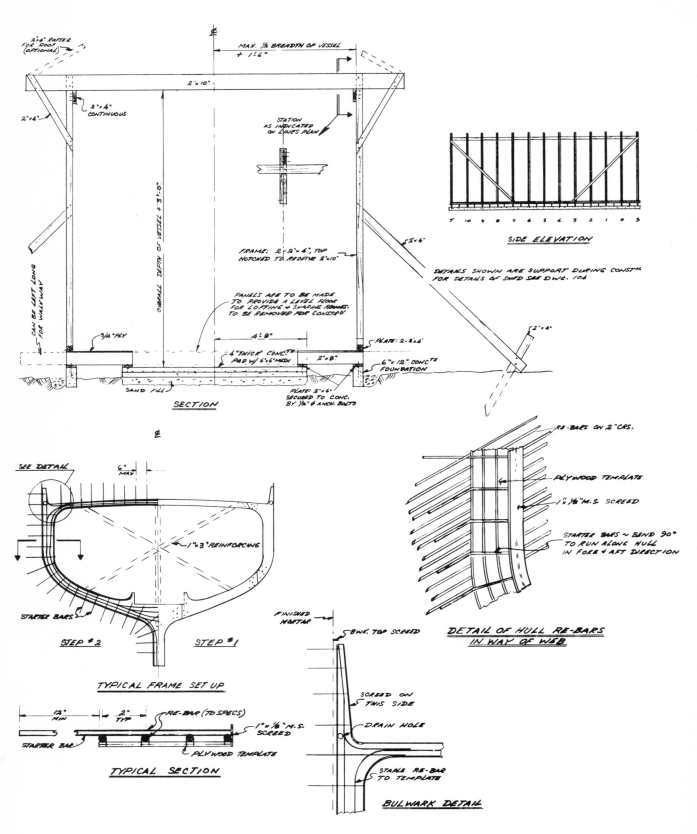

2"×4" RAFTER
FOR ROOF
(OPTIONAL)

MAX. ½ BREADTH OF VESSEL
+ 1'6"

2"×10"

3"×4"
CONTINUOUS

2"×4"

STATION
AS INDICATED
ON LINES PLAN

OPTIONAL HEIGHT OF VESSEL + 1'0"

CAN BE LEFT LONG
FOR WALKWAY

FRAME: 2-2"×4", TOP
NOTCHED TO RECEIVE 2"×10"

PANELS ARE TO BE MADE
TO PROVIDE A LEVEL FLOOR
FOR LOFTING & SHAPING FRAMES.
TO BE REMOVED FOR CONST'N

¾" PLY

4'-9"

4" THICK CONC'TE
PAD W/ 6"×6" MESH

2"×8"

PLATE: 2-2"×4"

6"×12" CONC'TE
FOUNDATION

SAND FILL

PLATE: 2"×6"
SECURED TO CONC.
BY ½" ∅ ANCH. BOLTS

SECTION

5"2"×4"

DETAILS SHOWN ARE SUPPORT DURING CONST'N
FOR DETAILS OF SHED SEE DWG. 10A

2"×4"

SIDE ELEVATION

T 10 9 8 7 6 5 4 3 2 1 0 5

RE-BARS ON 2" CRS.

PLYWOOD TEMPLATE

1"×⅛" M.S. SCREED

STARTER BARS ~ BEND 90°
TO RUN ALONG HULL
IN FORE & AFT DIRECTION

DETAIL OF HULL RE-BARS
IN WAY OF WEB

SEE DETAIL

6"
MAX

1"×3" REINFORCING

STARTER BARS

STEP #2

STEP #1

TYPICAL FRAME SET UP

12"
MIN

2"
TYP

RE-BAR (TO SPECS)

1"×⅛" M.S.
SCREED

STARTER BAR

PLYWOOD TEMPLATE

TYPICAL SECTION

FINISHED
MORTAR

BWK. TOP SCREED

SCREED ON
THIS SIDE

DRAIN HOLE

STAPLE RE-BAR
TO TEMPLATE

BULWARK DETAIL

for bracing. These shorts are allowed to protrude for about one foot beyond the outside edge.

Two more layers of the ½-inch 22 gauge chicken wire are now stapled on top of this re-bar framework with the inside edge again trimmed off neatly with the shears. And again, darts must be cut into the outside edge at 6-inch centres, the outside again being allowed to overlap for 6 inches.

In a medium-sized fishing vessel, these pre-formed webs would not be plastered at this stage. In a larger vessel, however, it might be considered advisable to plaster at this point and provide stiffening for the vessel during the remainder of the construction. In this case, the strap iron screeds would be replaced by three-quarter-inch by one-inch wooden screeds or whatever thickness of bulkhead is designed into the vessel. These web patterns would then be plastered right on the workshop floor.

Returning now to the troller, setting-up can commence. Using a waterline as a guide, lengths of 2"x12" lumber are attached to the frame patterns, and these are hung in position as shown in the drawing.

The next step is to shore-up a length of channel iron which will run along the straight run of the keel. This serves a number of purposes and provides an ideal grounding shoe. Sharp corners of mortar are inclined to chip and the channel iron eliminates this danger. The bottom of the keel has also proven a difficult area in which to achieve adequate penetration. The channel iron helps provide the finish and is a good stiff member to assist in the set-up and reduce movement throughout construction. When shored-up in place, this channel iron is welded to the web frames to ensure against shifting.

The channel iron is used along the straight length of the keel; where the sweep of the bow commences, a length of one-inch cold rolled steel rod is substituted. This is allowed to run wild beyond the sheer line and can be secured overhead to further stiffening.

The shaft log is now set-up and when this is complete the stern assembly is set up as also shown in the drawing.

After ensuring that the hull is fair, the task of welding the longitudinal lengths of ¼-inch reinforcing rod in place can begin. It will be found simplest to spot-weld the longitudinals first along the waterlines and then fill in with lengths on 2-inch centres. Quarter-inch re-bar ribs are then spot-welded into place vertically on 6-inch centres. Extra rods should be placed

in the stem area, parallel to the stem and about one-inch apart, for reinforcement.

Short rods are bent around the inside of the stem and welded in place as illustrated.

The wire mesh which was left protruding from the web frames will have been bent over to allow placement of the longitudinals. The two layers in each direction and the short rods protruding from these frames can also now be bent at right angles and welded into place. These should all be bent longitudinally, fore and aft, alternately.

It should perhaps also be pointed out at this stage that, as the deck is constructed in the same manner as the hull, the vertical rods forming ribs in the hull should be lapped in and welded to rods running athwartships on the deck. The longitudinal re-bar on the deck should follow the contour on two-inch centres. All bends and joints should have a minimum of a five-inch radius.

Hatch coamings, etc. should be finished off at this stage and edged with one-inch strap iron screeds.

While the overall thickness of the hull and deck will ideally be three-quarters of an inch, the one-inch screed is used to ensure that all stray ends of mesh can be well buried in the mortar.

The engine beds are next framed up before the 2"x12" lumber braces are removed. These lumber braces are removed one at a time and transferred to an overhead position, again see drawing. The hull is then braced to these lengths of lumber by pieces of re-bar attached to the deck.

The hull is now ready to receive the wire mesh— eight layers of the ½-inch 22 gauge chicken wire. Four layers are attached to each side of the rods. Mesh obtained in rolls 3'x150' will be found the easiest to work with. Desired lengths can be doubled and suspended from the sheer, ensuring that the joints are lapped. On the inside, the wire mesh must lap over the mesh on the web frames.

The mesh must be laced as tightly as possible, using tie wires or hog ring fasteners.

When the mesh is tightly laced, the ¾-inch wooden plywood patterns can be freed from the staples and the mesh secured on the webs. And, when the wire mesh is tightly laced all over, ¾-inch plywood wooden planks can be positioned for any through-hull fittings, deck fittings, limber holes, etc.

Braces are now placed under the bilges to eliminate any danger of distortion when the wet mortar is

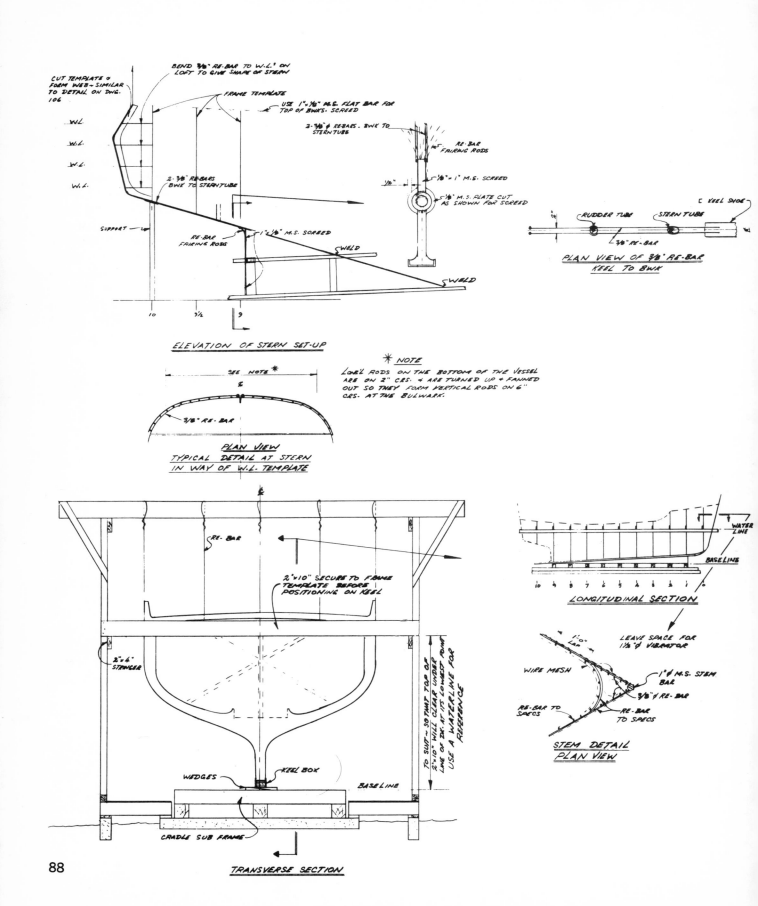

BEND ³/₈" RE-BAR TO W.L. ON
LOFT TO GIVE SHAPE OF STERN

CUT TEMPLATE &
FORM WEB~ SIMILAR
TO DETAIL ON DWG.
106

FRAME TEMPLATE

USE 1"×¹/₈" M.S. FLAT BAR FOR
TOP OF BWKS. SCREED

W.L.

2- ³/₈" Ø REBARS - BWK TO
STERN TUBE

W.L.

RE-BAR
FAIRING RODS

W.L.

2- ³/₈" REBARS
BWK TO STERNTUBE

¹/₈"

³/₈" × 1" M.S. SCREED

W.L.

⁵/₈" M.S. PLATE CUT
AS SHOWN FOR SCREED

SUPPORT

RE-BAR
FAIRING RODS

1"×¹/₈" M.S. SCREED

WELD

WELD

10   5¹/₂   9

ELEVATION OF STERN SET-UP

SEE NOTE *

³/₈" RE-BAR

PLAN VIEW
TYPICAL DETAIL AT STERN
IN WAY OF W.L. TEMPLATE

* NOTE

LONG'L RODS ON THE BOTTOM OF THE VESSEL
ARE ON 2" CRS. & ARE TURNED UP & FANNED
OUT SO THEY FORM VERTICAL RODS ON 6"
CRS. AT THE BULWARK.

RUDDER TUBE   STERN TUBE   KEEL SHOE

³/₈" RE-BAR

PLAN VIEW OF ³/₈" RE-BAR
KEEL TO BWK

RE-BAR

2"×10" SECURE TO FRAME
TEMPLATE BEFORE
POSITIONING ON KEEL

2"×4"
STRINGER

TO SUIT~ SO THAT TOP OF
2"×10" WILL CLEAR UNDER
LINE OF DK. AT ITS LOWEST POINT
USE A WATERLINE FOR
REFERENCE

WEDGES   KEEL BOX

BASELINE

CRADLE SUB FRAME

TRANSVERSE SECTION

WATER
LINE

BASELINE

10 9 8 7 6 5 4 3 2 1 0

LONGITUDINAL SECTION

LEAVE SPACE FOR
1¹/₂" Ø VIBRATOR

1'-0" LAP

WIRE MESH

1" Ø M.S. STEM
BAR

RE-BAR TO
SPECS

³/₈" Ø RE-BAR

RE-BAR
TO SPECS

STEM DETAIL
PLAN VIEW

applied. The hull framework is then well hosed to oxydize the mill-scale off the reinforcing bars.

Scaffolding must be rigged in preparation for the plastering.

The first part of the hull to be plastered is the keel, using a pencil vibrator to ensure penetration. This is followed by the underside of the decks and the webs.

The mortar is then applied to the inside of the hull and is squeezed through as thoroughly as possible, with the finish applied from the outside.

The top of the deck should be plastered one week later using a latex bonding agent. The coat applied to the underside will provide the necessary form for this.

The outside of the hull should be given a trowel finish. The temperature for the plastering work should be between 50-80 degrees and the wetting down process should begin after 24 hours. This will be carried out continuously for three weeks.

After this curing period, the outside of the hull should be etched with muriatic acid and well rinsed. Two coats of a thiokol-based epoxy resin are then applied to protect any stray ends of wire mesh which may be protruding. The hull can then of course be painted to suit, again using an epoxy paint on the topsides and vinyl anti-fouling.

The wooden cabin is to be through-bolted into position and all deck-fittings will be bolted into place using hardwood backing blocks.

The fish hold will be insulated with sheet styrofoam glued onto the inside of the hull. One layer of wire mesh can be applied over this and plastered, allowing the inside of the hold to be easily cleaned.

The fuel tanks and water tanks will be constructed from mild steel.

The forepeak of the vessel can also be lined with the styrofoam covered with a white vinyl. Spruce sparring can be placed over this to provide a warm, clean fo'c'sle.

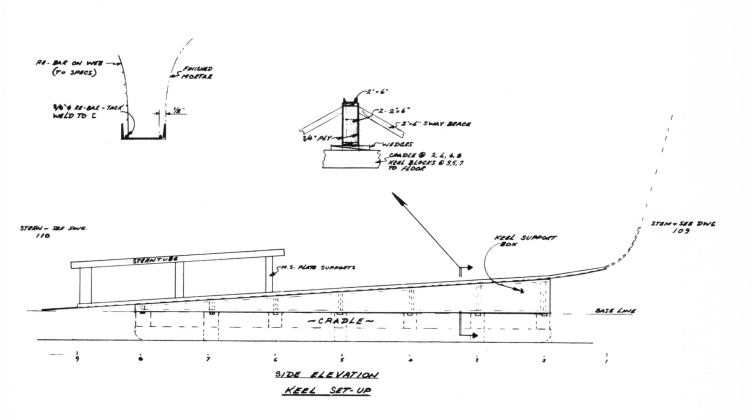

SIDE ELEVATION
KEEL SET-UP

CHAPTER 12

ALTERNATE DECK TECHNIQUE

Experiments with the cedar mold technique have produced an improved method for the builder who wishes to cast in his deck and toe-rails the same day that he completes his hull. This also gives the added advantage of strengthening the hull during the rolling process. It is now being adopted by the majority of builders.

The decision whether or not to cast in the deck and toe-rails must be taken early as special provisions have to be made when cutting the frames on the loft floor. As the frames are lifted from the loft, special bracing is attached running from the bilge through where the deck cutout will be, to the deck beam which has been cut in reverse. This bracing is well nailed or bolted (see diagram).

An additional cross brace is put in about one foot above the deck cut-out running horizontally across the frame to add further strength.

Later, a cut-out of two and three-quarter inches is to be made through the frame at the deck line and these braces will give required support.

The molds are now set up as earlier detailed and planking commenced. The first plank is set level with the top of the deck beam and planking continues downwards until it is at least two inches below the sheer line. Two or three planks are all that are normally required for this. Be sure to choose the longest and straightest planks for this—you are establishing a very important line.

The gap must now be left and this is done along the full length of the boat by using a two-and-three-quarter inch block. The gap runs continuously even from stem to stern and around the transom. Continue planking upwards in the normal manner until the bend becomes too severe to allow the planks to lay in without extreme shingling at the midships section.

Now is the time to put in the deck planking. You still have plenty of light in the hull and it is easy to get into and work inside the inverted framework.

We now cut the gap in the frame and this is easily done by laying the saw flat along the deck beam from the inside and following the camber to the end of the beam. Moving up the required two-and-three inches to the underside of the first run of planking the cut is made inwards, running up at a good angle to leave working room for later lay-up and plastering.

The planking of the deck can now begin using nominal 1″ x 2″ planks. Starting at the stem, the first plank is laid on top of the planks which will form the toe-rail. This plank is well nailed home into position and is pulled in to follow the curve of the deck along to the stem. This plank must be bullnosed later so care must be taken with the positioning of the nails—in fact, it is a good idea to bullnose first and avoid the later chore of countersinking many of the nails.

Planking continues along the deck until the cabin and cockpit cut-out points are passed. At the stem (and stern where necessary) the planks are set in a herring-bone pattern.

Prior to this planking, it is a good idea to place a board in position along the centre line of the boat at the stem and stern. As the planks come through and are trimmed into the herring-bone pattern, or mitred, they can be nailed down onto the board (see diagram).

When the deck is completely nailed in place and bullnosed (see diagram) one-inch square screeds are attached at the cabin, cockpit and hatch cut-outs and along the top of the toe-rail. Take great care to ensure that these screeds are fair—they will be the finished lines which the eye will see when the boat is in the water.

The vapour barrier is now applied over the deck, lapping over the joint and down to the toe-rail. Four layers of chicken wire can next be stapled in place from screed to screed. These layers must be trimmed off neatly at the screeds.

Reinforcing bars are next stapled in place, two inches apart, running from stem to stern. These are allowed to run wild at the bow and stern for six inches or a foot.

A vapour barrier is now tacked in place along the first few planks running upwards from the gap. This should be at least a foot or one foot and a half in height.

Reinforcing bars are stapled in place on six-inch centres athwartships. They butt up neatly against the cabin, cockpit and hatch screeds on the interior but are allowed to run wild for at least a foot as they protrude through the gap. A number of these bars will of course run completely across the deck and run wild at each side.

Before the reinforcing bars are turned into place alongside the hull four more layers of chicken wire are fastened into place. Again this mesh is allowed to run wild for about a foot or foot-and-a-half where it protrudes through the gap. This is first bent upwards and stapled against the hull. Then the protruding reinforcing bars can also be bent upwards and firmly fastened.

After the rest of the hull planking has been completed normal lay-up continues around the hull overlapping the upturned chicken wire and rods. The full length vertical rods running down the hull side are carried down to the toe-rail screed to give the required strength in the toe-rail.

Plastering of the hull and deck is carried out in the usual way and it will be found not too difficult to work inside the hull to complete the decks.

The builder is virtually guaranteed 100 per cent penetration on a horizontal area such as the deck if a vibrator is used.

It is almost certain that future developments in ferro-cement boat building will make it possible for builders to leave the wooden mold in place in their boat if required. This will give a neat wooden lined interior, substitute bulkheads for molds, simplify interior finishing and contribute extra strength to the hull itself.

Until this stage is reached, however, provision must now be made in the lay-up to complete interior webs when the mold is taken out. This is done as follows. From the inside of the boat a long extension drill is laid alongside the molds where the web will be positioned. Wherever possible, S.M.D.E. plans place interior webs on station positions but it is sometimes necessary to make up an in-between mold to accommodate a desired feature in the boat's general arrangement.

Holes are drilled on six-inch centres from keel to deck. This is done of course before any outside lay-up has started. Now from the outside a length of chicken wire, two feet in width, is folded four times. A strip of the plastic vapour barrier is inserted into the middle folds of this mesh. This is to prevent the mortar reaching the last two layers of mesh as they will be later folded into the boat and lashed to protruding rods. The rods made in two foot lengths are bent at right angles and pushed through the pre-drilled holes. They run horizontally on the outside of the boat— alternated one forward and one aft. These are not put in place until the last four layers of chicken wire and vapour barrier are applied to the outside of the hull.

This same process must be repeated on the deck inside the hull to act as deck beams. Drilling will not of course be necessary here as the right-angle rods can simply be stapled into place.

To ensure a fair and neatly finished web on the inside the protruding rods must all be trimmed off at uniform length. This is best done by preparing a plywood template for the corners of the webs and using a board approximately one foot by five inches down the side of the hull. After all the rods are trimmed neatly a one inch strap iron screed can be spot welded to the ends. Rods running completely around the hull are now tied in about two inches apart and the chicken wire is folded in from the hull, trimmed off and tied. The four layers of chicken wire are sufficient for these webs.

After the webs have been cemented in the normal manner, plywood bulkheads and lockers, etc. can be attached by bolts.

Extra reinforcing is sometimes required in the stem area and this can be achieved simply by laying in extra lengths of three-eighths reinforcing bar on two inch centres. These should run from the stem right into the keel.

It should also be noted that in some designs it is not always possible to build up a complete lumber mold into the keel area. This is because it would be too difficult to remove the wood after plastering. In such cases, the keel is welded up and constructed in the regular pipe framework method.

Also on some hulls, the cabin cut-out does not extend too far towards the stem. This means that bracing has to be left in during plastering. Holes left by these braces can be filled later when the wood is removed.

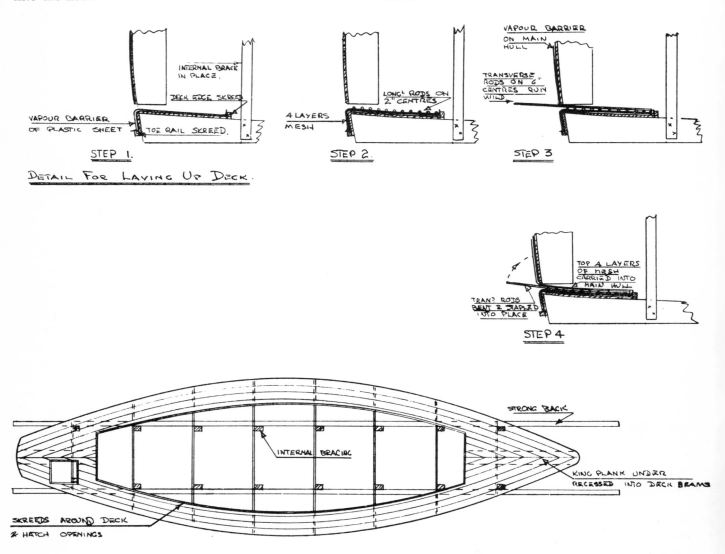

CHAPTER 13

MISCELLANEOUS TIPS

We feel it is advisable to have stiffening bulkheads throughout the ferro-cement boat. These bulkheads need not be large but should protrude far enough into the interior of the hull to afford some stiffness.

If a bulkhead is to be put in we feel it should also be continuous starting from the floor in the bilge to form a knee under the side deck. The method of inserting these bulkheads or stiffening member is simple. A ¼″ mild steel reinforcing bar is bent almost to a right angle. This is laid alongside the longitudinal bars so the right angle protrudes into the interior at an angle which will line up with a similar bulkhead installed on the opposite side of the hull.

These bulkheads should range between 6″ and 1-foot in width and should form a continuous fair bend. There is no reason in this type of construction to have the bulkheads go completely across the boat unless they are installed for other reasons than structural strength amidships. These bulkheads should be finished with a 1″ mild steel skreed. This is a strip of metal to run the trowel along when plastering. They should be installed plumb to the cabin sole to facilitate fastening wood partitions to them at a later date. The majority of the interior joinery is landed on these bulkheads or partitions.

Where hanging knees are suspended to support the side decks, they should be tapered into the deck and into the hull in a fair curve. These should be installed in the same way as the bulkheads using short rods running at least 6″ to 1-foot along the longitudinal rods. Because of the weight factor in ferro-cement boats, the size of the bulkheads and hanging knees should be kept to a minimum.

Installing the Engine:

The shaft log itself should be installed at the same time as the hull is plastered. To install this, it is advisable to have a piece of shafting the same size as the propeller shaft or the propeller shaft itself. The bearing and stuffing blocks should be assembled to the stern tube and the shaft slid into this. The whole assembly should then be lined up to the centre line of the boat, with consideration given to the engine's eventual bedding place. This assembly may have to be tilted up in the forward end if the engine itself will not sit horizontally in that part of the bilge where it is designed to go. On sailboats, the bilge flares out very quickly in this area and raising the forward end a couple of inches usually gives a lot of width in the area of the engine bearers.

Once everything is lined up satisfactorily and the engine will fit into the area left, the propeller shaft is fastened, making sure that stop waters, etc. have been installed. It is then plastered in position when the hull is plastered.

To line up the engine itself and install the engine

For the ferro-cement salmon troller "Lady Silica" (left), a sister-ship. This sleek 42-footer was also built in Victoria, Canada, by Gordon Ellis. The two boats are now out earning their keep in Canadian waters.

beds, it is easiest to suspend the engine from a chain block. The coupling to the propeller shaft is connected using feller gauges to ensure reasonable alignment. Channel iron engine bearers are bolted to the lugs left on the bottom of the engine for this purpose. A 1″ minimum hardwood block should be bolted between the lugs and the bearers and anchor bolts suspended through holes drilled into the bottom of the channel iron.

Once this has been completed, a small plywood form is put in, travelling from the side of the engine bearer, plumb to the bottom of the boat, running the length of the engine bearer and filled with cement. This forms a very rigid base for the engine. The area between the engine bearers can be dyked off and this forms an excellent sump into which any oil or fuel leakage from the engine gathers, preventing contamination of the rest of the bilge.

During construction, some starter rods should be left protruding from the hull in the same manner as they are left for bulkheads.

Also, before the engine bearers are cemented in the hull, this area should be well etched in order to facilitate a good bond between the new and old mortar. If the engine to be installed is for a work boat, it is advisable to fabricate two beams in the approximate area of the engine bearers running fore and aft with starter rods coming up off each vertical rod and repeat the performance in much the same way as when installing an engine in an auxillary sailboat.

There is a lot of vibration in the engine of a power boat especially when a large powerful engine is installed. Vibrations and strains imposed on the engine bed often increase greatly if there is damage to the propeller or shaft. The engine bed should be of a sufficient bulk to absorb this shock and on a power boat it would not hurt to have the engine bed running 20% of the length of the hull.

The weight of the bulk of the engine bed is not normally too critical for a pleasure or work boat. It is installed in the area where normally ballast would be inserted to keep her stable.

Gudgeons and pintles are installed through a deadwood. One disadvantage of ferro-cement construction is the difficulty of changing things once they have been cast into the concrete. So, when installing the gudgeons and pintles on a sailboat it is wise to have the rudder made up complete before the hull is plastered. The gudgeons should be made up and fitted to the hull using a dowling of the same diameter as the bolt which will eventually hold on these fittings. The chicken wire in this area is usually bulky enough to keep the dowling in place. Once the location of the gudgeons is determined, the dowling is slipped through the bolt holes and they are cut off flush with the surface of the chicken wire and left in place throughout plastering. These can be knocked out later and will make the job of fastening the gudgeons much easier. Mocking up the rudder before plastering will not only facilitate the gudgeon installation but will also allow a check on the alignment of the rudder tube. The rudder must swing free. It is easier to correct at this stage than when everything is plastered solid.

Through Hull Fittings and Port Holes:

These should be blanked out before plastering. The through hull fittings are normally of two sizes, 1½ and ¾. A good idea of where these fittings will protrude through the hull is required before the boat is plastered. Three-quarter inch plywood circles cut out using a hole saw are used for the through hull fittings. These can be wired to the hull flush with the chicken wire on the outside. Through hull fittings should be purchased before these are cut to ensure the inserts are the same size as the fittings themselves. The same applies for the dead-lights. Once the size and shape of the dead-lights are determined, they are cut out of ¾" plywood with a ½" x ½" lip notched into the plywood with a router. These can also be wired in position with care taken to keep them lined up. The flange should show to the outside and this will develop a flange on the inside on plastering day.

Plywood must be straight and not warped. If warped plywood is used, warped glass is also needed! It is really difficult to find any glass that will fit into a jamb that has a wind in it!

The best type of glass to install into dead-lights is a plate glass of at least ⅜" thickness, preferably ½". If ½" glass is used, blanks must be of sufficient thickness to receive the glass and also leave a ⅜" lip. Plywood of this size is not usually obtainable so it is easier to laminate up two layers, one cut ⅜ smaller than the other around the circumference. The area where the glass fits should be ½" or larger and the rabbet should be formed with ⅜" plywood. The glass itself can be set in using any one of the several types of very sticky bedding compound on the market today. Silica sealer is a good one. Once the glass has been set into an excess of bedding compound, a narrow strip of epoxy can be applied to the circumference of the dead-light hole on the hull surface and a thin strip of cement used as a glass stop on the outside.

Opening ports which are to be installed into the side of the hull are best blanked off to the neat size of the porthole itself and fastened into position. The through bolt holes required to attach these ports are easier drilled out later using a carbide tipped drill. When installing any bolts through the concrete shell, a larger washer or backing plate should be used on the inside. The bolts themselves should be set into a non-hardening bedding compound and an oakum or cotton grommet should be wrapped around the bolt where it goes through the hull from the outside. This grommet tends to swell when in contact with moisture, thus blocking off the hole from any annoying leaks.

The chain plates should be located in position before plastering. When making up the chain plates and drilling the holes which fasten them to the hull, a backing chain plate is made up at the same time so that the holes correspond. The backing chain plate should be made from the same material as the chain plates themselves—also, the bolts. This can be mild steel galvanized, cast bronze (a brass backing plate will do there for bronze) or stainless steel of the salt water resistant variety.

Skreeds:

It is very difficult to plaster a finished edge straight without the use of a skreed. Some builders use wooden skreeds lashed to the edges which are to be left finished, such as toe rails, scuppers, bulkheads, stem, deadwoods, etc. In our experience it has been found more practical to fabricate these skreeds from mild steel galvanized. When concrete ends in a square corner it is quite prone to chipping. Metal skreeds protect these corners and also act as a finishing strip. Galvanized metal is quite difficult to weld because of sputtering but it can be done. All extruding edges of cement which come to a hard corner should be finished in this way. This will make neat, clean corners.

Pipe wrapped with chicken wire is very difficult to finish neatly even for a professional plasterer, so it is best to avoid pipe protrusions above the deck. Beware here of pipes which have been used for interior bulkheads.

On finished corners such as in fishboats hold dividers, ready-made corner beading used by plasterers in house construction is handy, to produce a finished and professional job.

Deck fittings, etc., can be mounted in much the same method as chain plates but if there is to be a heavy strain on the fitting, it must be well backed up from underneath using either a hardwood block or a piece of similar metal.

Fuel and Water Tanks:

Fuel and water tanks may be included as integral parts of the ferro-cement hull. There are several advantages and disadvantages to this.

One obvious disadvantage is that if the tanks become fouled, they are sometimes difficult to reach for thorough cleaning.

Secondly, if the hull receives damage in the area of a tank it may be quite difficult to repair—particularly unless an access hole has been left for such an emergency.

The advantages are just as obvious. Concrete tanks constructed as integral parts of the hull form very, very economical units. The baffles can be easily constructed and the ends of the tanks themselves form webs in the bilge of the boat which act as good stiffening members, and don't hurt the boat structurally.

Water left in a concrete container remains quite sweet. Diesel fuel, kerosene, and gasoline are similarly unaffected by storage in concrete.

The only fuel which could possibly damage the concrete is the diesel oil which contains a low concentration of sulphur but this can be prevented by coating the interior of the tanks with two layers of epoxy resin set in fiberglass cloth. This seals the surface of

the concrete and bonds any fine particles of dust or sand which may remain in the bottom of the tanks and cause trouble to the engine.

Diesel fuel seems able to seep through any material more readily than water and the epoxy would take care of any problems which might develop over the years. All tanks must be lined.

Adequate drainage must be left when installing tanks in the bottom of the hull. Bilge water should run freely to a sump aft. In general, ferro-cement boats are quite watertight but stuffing boxes etc. are prone to leakage and whenever there are a lot of openings in the boat, water usually works itself in.

The baffles may be installed into the tanks by attaching them to the lid of the inspection plate. The inspection plate itself should be of mild steel bolted to the concrete by a flange. Studs should be left protruding through the concrete to receive this flange. This should be bedded down using a neophrene gasket and plenty of bedding compound.

Tips on Handling Wood:

Wood is beautiful. There is probably no natural material with the same esthetic appeal. Wood grain is imitated in plastic laminates, vinyl covering and many other ways, but there is nothing that actually matches the warmth of the genuine thing.

The following are a few points to remember in using wood:
1. Plywood should always have the end sealed with red lead or some other type of wood sealer.
2. All joints should be glued, screwed or bolted to prevent them coming apart.
3. Whenever wood is in contact with concrete or steel, a bedding compound should be used.
4. The wood should also be treated with a good preservative.

While on the subject of bedding compounds it is best to select a compound which will remain flexible indefinitely. Wood has a large expansion and contraction rate while concrete is quite low in comparison. The bedding compound should be flexible enough to expand and contract keeping joints watertight at all times. Wood should be dry and clean before the application of fiberglass, celastic, dynel, or paint.

When purchasing wood, care should be taken to

check for a short grain, sap wood, and knots. Always plane or sand wood in such a way that the grain is laid flat. It is easy to judge the lay of the grain by lightly rubbing a finger up and down the edge of the board to be planed. Always plane with the grain. All woods should be sealed before painting or varnishing.

On wood which is to be varnished, a clear sealer or a staining sealer should be used, depending on the desired result. Before applying plastic laminates to wood, all nail holes and knot holes must be filled and the surface which is to receive the plastic laminate should be as smooth and flat as possible with all joints sanded flush.

It is a good practice to prime the wood surface by applying an extra coat of contact cement. The final coat used in applying a plastic laminate contains a solvent which will partially dissolve the prime coat. This ensures a good bond. It is also good practice when using plywood to avoid showing end-grain. A square corner piece of wood or molding will cover this. If insulation is being used, such as styrofoam against wood, it must be covered with plywood on both sides. This should be liberally glued to fill any voids not filled by the insulation itself.

The glue will seal the insulation and help stop it absorbing moisture. If all air is excluded from the area, dry rot will not start as easily.

In the interior of a boat, condensation is sometimes a problem and if insulation is stuffed between the deck beams without the protection of sealing, dry rot starts very quickly.

Avoid pockets in the boat where water can collect such as mast steps, cupboard bottoms, etc. Be sure drain holes are of sufficient size to prevent plugging with the dust and trash which gathers in the bottom of inaccessible lockers, etc.

The most important factor in wood construction is ventilation. Ventilate everywhere, allowing free passage of air around all deck beams, bulkheads, cupboards, and bunk bottoms. This will keep the boat fresh and give the wood fittings a much longer life. Ventilation is the surest cure for condensation.

Smooth in line and a sturdy performer. This is the "Analani", designed, built and owned by Wilf O'Kell who now builds ferro-cement boats in Mackay, Australia. A sister-ship to the 50-foot "Analani" has been built in Hamilton, New Zealand.

Picking up Lines and making Molds:

There are many different ways in which lines can be picked up from the loft floor and earlier in the book we suggested the use of a pick-up board. Another method, surprisingly effective in its simplicity, involves the use of carpet tacks or large thin headed nails.

The tacks or nails are simply placed along the length of the mold line on the loft floor. The head of the tack or nail is placed right on this line and tapped smartly into place (see Page 73). These nails are placed about four inches apart with the pointed ends of the nails laying outward.

The wooden board from which you are going to cut the mold is now placed on top of these nails. Step carefully onto the board and leave a clear imprint of the nail heads on the underside. Now, turning the board over you can join up the marks with a pencil line using a batten to ensure you achieve a fair line.

With each mold you have of course to produce two identical pieces so the next step is to nail another board to the first one and cut out to the established line on a band saw or with a hand power saw.

It is impossible to cut out a mold on one complete board so a number of pieces have to be scabbed together. As soon as you complete the first two pieces of the mold jigsaw put them in place on the loft floor and cut the next two.

Where the two halves of the mold join at the keel they should be butted right on the centerline of the vessel.

Assembling and scabbing together of the complete mold when all the pieces are cut is done in two operations. Scab one half together and flip this over so that the butts are underneath. Now assemble the second half on top of this. This confirms the uniformity of the pieces and ensures that the scabs or butts are on the same side of the mold when it is assembled on the strongback.

It is now a good idea to put the completed mold back on the loft floor and mark in the sheer, water lines, diagonals and buttocks. These are handy reference points when setting up the frame and fairing.

The two pieces of the mold can now be put together with a scab or butt at the keel and a one piece deck pattern beam. A few additional braces are added for rigidity and the mold can be carefully numbered and stored against the shed wall until required.

A Cast Keel:

Experience has shown that a cast keel is often desirable when building with a pipe framework or a modified wooden framework in the upright position. With the boat sitting upright it has proved next to impossible to achieve 100 percent plaster penetration on the underside of the keel.

The answer is to pre-cast this keel section as the first step. Ideally this section should be about four inches in depth so this must first be cut off the bottom of the pipe or wooden station frames. Now we must make up a mold in which to cast the keel. The shape of the bottom of the keel is lofted and a pattern cut for this in three-quarter-inch board. This is laid down. **Remember however to cut this board three-quarters of an inch larger than the lofted size.** This will allow for the thickness of the skin. This board is now laid down and sides are attached along the full length. To achieve the four-inch depth inside this casting box the side board should be four-and-three quarter inches in depth. These sides can be braced by nails or scrap pieces of lumber from the top of the sides to the floor.

It is now advisable to round off the bottom of the keel box on the inside to prevent chipping of the keel. This is done by setting plaster or polyfilla in the inside edges. The full mold should now be well oiled.

Two layers of chicken wire are laid inside this keel box, overlapping the edges by about six inches. On top of this are laid heavy reinforcing bars running the full length of the box and protruding at stem and stern. The size of this reinforcing rod is dictated by the size of the vessel under construction.

Boards are nailed across the top of the keel box at the station points where the molds will later attach to the keel itself. To each of these boards a length of strap iron, pre-bolted for later attachment to the actual mold, is tacked. This strap will extend down into the keel itself as a joining point.

The pre-cast keel will also be joined to the remainder of the framework by numerous starter rods and these are positioned in the keel box on approximate six-inch centres. We can now pour our cement and vibrate well into the casting box. When the cement has cured, the wooden mold can be stripped away and any excess oil wiped clear.

The pre-cast keel is next turned over and checked for penetration. If all is okay and no patching up required the bottom of the keel can be given its coat of epoxy and later the anti-fouling added.

To all intents and purposes the keel can now be ignored completely. She is turned back into place and the boat set-up continues joining the rods from the hull to the starter rods from the keel. Special half-inch starter rods in the keel can be used to set inside the pipes where the pipe framework technique is being used. These joints should all be welded. The double layer of chicken wire protruding from the keel is also laced into position.

On the plastering day, this cement keel section should have special attention with at least another solid four-inch layer of concrete covering the top of the pre-cast keel.

Planking:

One of the biggest problems when planking a mold or plug is to prevent shingling of the boards. This can easily be achieved by using long strips of quarter-inch plywood nailed to the inside of the boards in between the station molds. This acts as a frame and stops the planking from lapping (see illustration on page 78).

Three or four layers of planking should be put in place before attaching the plywood strips. When the planking becomes too difficult to lay in, usually around the load water line, begin planking from one of the diagonals along the middle of the bottom of the boat. The ends of these planks are attached to the other planking with butt blocks.

Mesh:

Mesh should always be kept neat. If trouble is experienced in getting the mesh to lay up neatly a few darts are cut into the wire to allow it to follow the curves of the boat. This should be done with caution and only where it is impossible to get the wire to lay in neatly.

A dart prevents a wrinkle occurring but does cause a build-up in mesh thickness. With too much mesh build-up, penetration may become difficult.

Epoxy Skin:

An epoxy skin is almost an essential on any ferro-cement boat providing a perfect seal for any stray ends of mesh which may have been bared in the rubbing-down process. There are several types of epoxy

on the market but again experience has shown that the thiokol-based product is the best for the job.

This should be mixed with cabo-sil which acts as a thickening agent and is then applied with a trowel or putty knife. The hull must be bone dry prior to this application. If the wooden mold technique has been used in construction together with a vapor barrier, and if the wooden lining has been retained in the hull, it is essential to allow the outer skin to dry for several months. The drying-out process is much longer when the mold and vapor barrier are retained. Before application, be sure that the job is perfectly clean.

Care should also be exercised in the use of epoxy. It is very sticky, ruins clothes and can be damaging to skin and eyes. It should be mixed up in small batches and applied quickly in temperatures between 60 - 80 degrees. Normal working time is between 10 and 20 minutes.

An epoxy paint can be used over the epoxy skin on the top sides with a vinyl anti-fouling on the bottom.

At the builder's discretion, a two-ounce cloth can be used with the epoxy to assist bonding.

It should also be remembered that epoxy gives a smooth finish and a smooth finish will tend to emphasize any bumps or unfairness in a hull. Be sure the hull is faired to your satisfaction before applying the skin coat.

Finally, if a tar-based epoxy is used take special care—it is difficult to prevent the tar bleeding through a white paint finish.

Turning Boats:

The turning of the hull after construction in the cedar mold method is certainly one problem which worries many builders. It shouldn't. A number of methods have been evolved and probably the simplest and safest of these is rolling the hull in the water.

Actually the hull and the strongback on which it has been built are rolled at the same time. To one side of the hull or strongback, along its full length, should be attached empty drums or containers. This side of the strongback or hull is then attached firmly to a point on the shore or jetty with the lines running **underneath** the hull. Further lines are next attached to the opposite side of hull or strongback and these allowed to run **over** the boat, ideally to a point on an opposite jetty or shore. These are the lines which are pulled steadily forcing the hull, strongback and attached drums down beneath the surface. The lines attached earlier beneath the structure prevent it drifting towards the pullers. Passing through the centerpoint of the turning motion, the underwater drums will assist in turning the structure through its 360 degree circle into an upright position. Any water shipped during the operation can easily be pumped out.

Smaller hulls can be turned easily by dumping them onto bales of hay which have been tied together to give a soft bed. Some commercial builders do this successfully by using a fork lift to lever the hull over. Care must be taken of course not to damage the hull. Old tires could be used in place of the bales of hay if preferred.

Finally of course, a mobile crane can be brought in to turn a hull if the terrain is suitable. This will lower the keel to the ground with much more control and when the boat is on its side, lines can be attached to lift it into a cradle.

A C-Breeze hull, built in Honolulu, Hawaii, is safely rolled with the assistance of a mobile crane using the technique illustrated above.

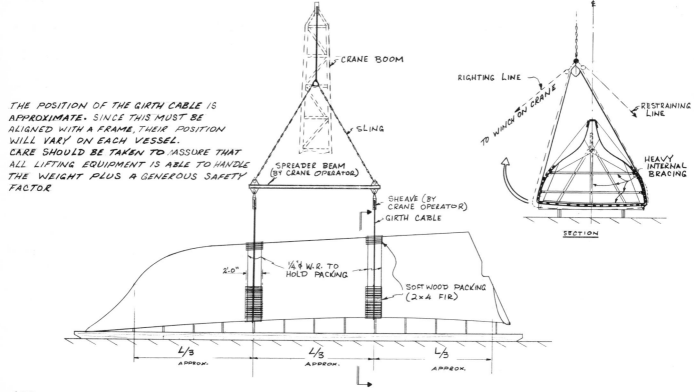

THE POSITION OF THE GIRTH CABLE IS APPROXIMATE. SINCE THIS MUST BE ALIGNED WITH A FRAME, THEIR POSITION WILL VARY ON EACH VESSEL.
CARE SHOULD BE TAKEN TO ASSURE THAT ALL LIFTING EQUIPMENT IS ABLE TO HANDLE THE WEIGHT PLUS A GENEROUS SAFETY FACTOR

CRANE BOOM

SLING

SPREADER BEAM (BY CRANE OPERATOR)

SHEAVE (BY CRANE OPERATOR)
GIRTH CABLE

2'-0"

¼"∅ W.R. TO HOLD PACKING

SOFTWOOD PACKING (2 x 4 FIR)

L/3 APPROX.
L/3 APPROX.
L/3 APPROX.

RIGHTING LINE

TO WINCH ON CRANE

RESTRAINING LINE

HEAVY INTERNAL BRACING

SECTION

CHAPTER 14

DETAIL DRAWINGS

No matter what medium, the art of boat building calls for a number of skills. None of these however, are beyond the average handyman and, to assist the amateur building for the first time in ferro-cement, Samson Marine Design Enterprises of Canada have produced with their plans a series of standard detail construction drawings which cover a variety of requirements. A few of these detail drawings are included in this next chapter and serve to show the thought and thoroughness which goes into a ferro-cement boat design. Many of these drawings depict typical stages of boat construction modified to the ferro-cement medium.

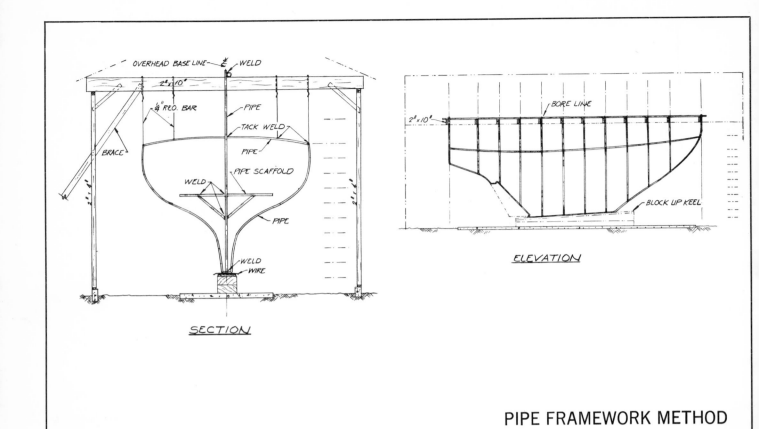

OVERHEAD BASE LINE — C WELD

2" x 10"

1/4" REO. BAR

PIPE

TACK WELD

PIPE

BRACE

PIPE SCAFFOLD

WELD

PIPE

WELD

WIRE

SECTION

BORE LINE

2" x 10"

BLOCK UP KEEL

ELEVATION

PIPE FRAMEWORK METHOD

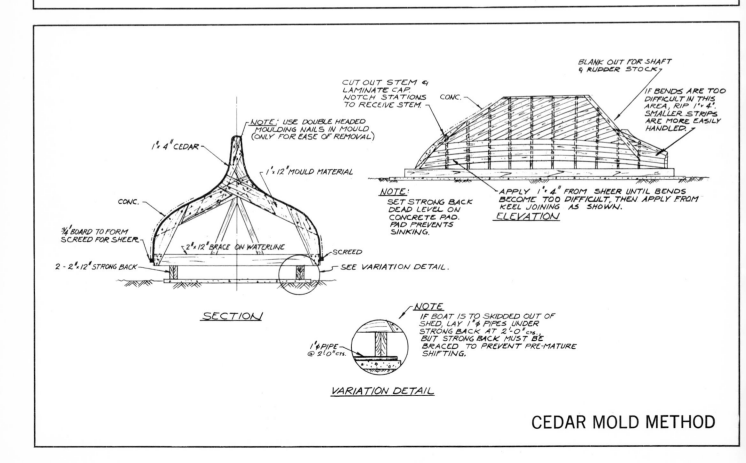

CUT OUT STEM &
LAMINATE CAP.
NOTCH STATIONS
TO RECEIVE STEM.

NOTE: USE DOUBLE HEADED
MOULDING NAILS IN MOULD
(ONLY FOR EASE OF REMOVAL)

1" x 4" CEDAR

1" x 12" MOULD MATERIAL

CONC.

3/4" BOARD TO FORM
SCREED FOR SHEER.

2" x 12" BRACE ON WATERLINE

2 - 2" x 12" STRONG BACK

SCREED

SEE VARIATION DETAIL.

SECTION

NOTE:
SET STRONG BACK
DEAD LEVEL ON
CONCRETE PAD.
PAD PREVENTS
SINKING.

BLANK OUT FOR SHAFT
& RUDDER STOCK

CONC.

IF BENDS ARE TOO
DIFFICULT IN THIS
AREA, RIP 1" x 4"
SMALLER STRIPS
ARE MORE EASILY
HANDLED.

APPLY 1" x 4" FROM SHEER UNTIL BENDS
BECOME TOO DIFFICULT, THEN APPLY FROM
KEEL JOINING AS SHOWN.

ELEVATION

NOTE
IF BOAT IS TO SKIDDED OUT OF
SHED, LAY 1"∅ PIPES UNDER
STRONG BACK AT 2'-0" cts.
BUT STRONG BACK MUST BE
BRACED TO PREVENT PRE-MATURE
SHIFTING.

1"∅ PIPE
@ 2'-0" cts.

VARIATION DETAIL

CEDAR MOLD METHOD

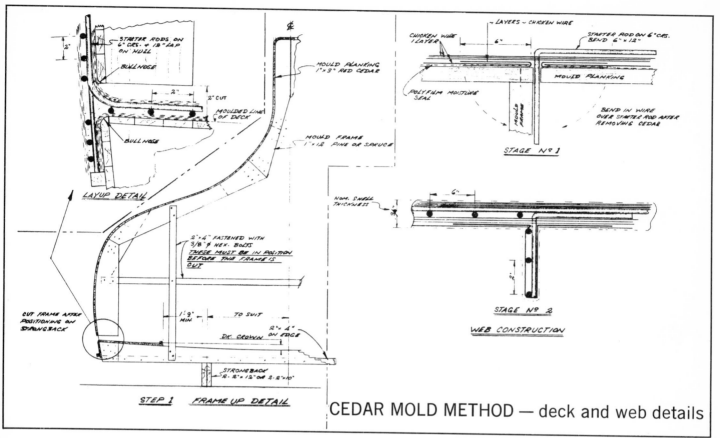

CEDAR MOLD METHOD — deck and web details

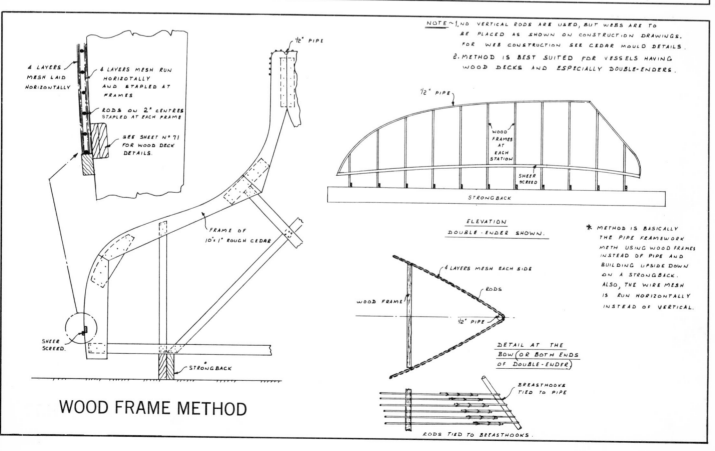

WOOD FRAME METHOD

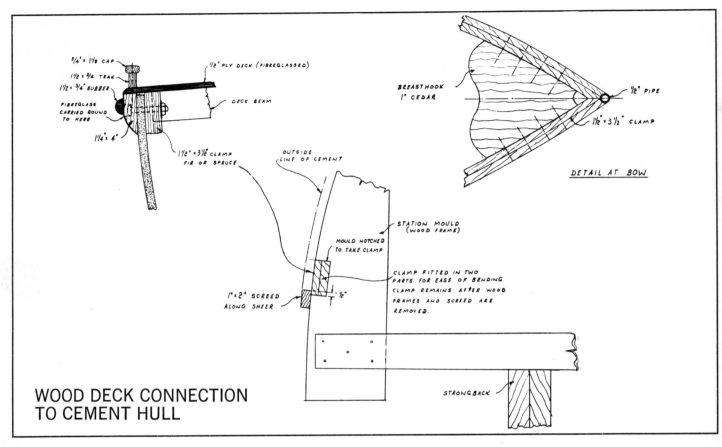

9/4" x 1 1/8" CAP
1 1/2" x 3/4" TEAK
1 1/2" x 3/4" RUBBER
FIBREGLASS CARRIED ROUND TO HERE
1 1/4" x 4"
1/2" PLY DECK (FIBREGLASSED)
DECK BEAM
1 1/2" x 3 1/2" CLAMP FIR OR SPRUCE
OUTSIDE LINE OF CEMENT
MOULD NOTCHED TO TAKE CLAMP
1" x 2" SCREED ALONG SHEER
1/4"
STATION MOULD (WOOD FRAME)
CLAMP FITTED IN TWO PARTS FOR EASE OF BENDING CLAMP REMAINS AFTER WOOD FRAMES AND SCREED ARE REMOVED.
STRONGBACK

BREASTHOOK 1" CEDAR
1/2" PIPE
1 1/2" x 3 1/2" CLAMP
DETAIL AT BOW

WOOD DECK CONNECTION TO CEMENT HULL

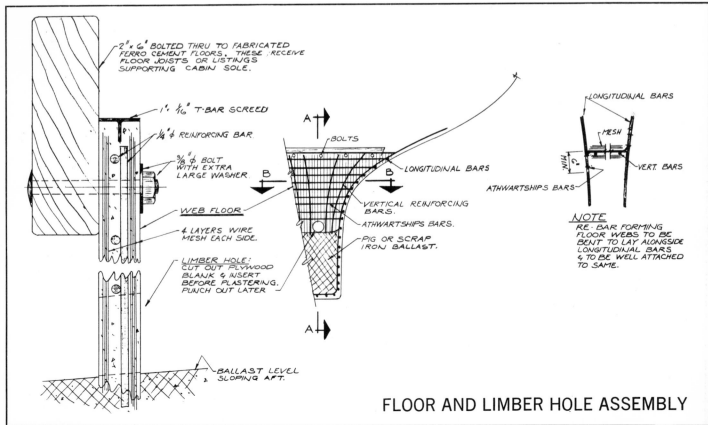

2" x 6" BOLTED THRU TO FABRICATED FERRO CEMENT FLOORS. THESE RECEIVE FLOOR JOISTS OR LISTINGS SUPPORTING CABIN SOLE.

1"x 1/16" T·BAR SCREED
1/4" Ø REINFORCING BAR.
3/8" Ø BOLT WITH EXTRA LARGE WASHER.
WEB FLOOR
4 LAYERS WIRE MESH EACH SIDE.
LIMBER HOLE: CUT OUT PLYWOOD BLANK & INSERT BEFORE PLASTERING. PUNCH OUT LATER
BALLAST LEVEL SLOPING AFT.

BOLTS
LONGITUDINAL BARS
VERTICAL REINFORCING BARS.
ATHWARTSHIPS BARS.
PIG OR SCRAP IRON BALLAST.

LONGITUDINAL BARS
MESH
VERT. BARS
ATHWARTSHIPS BARS
1" MIN.

NOTE
RE·BAR FORMING FLOOR WEBS TO BE BENT TO LAY ALONGSIDE LONGITUDINAL BARS & TO BE WELL ATTACHED TO SAME.

FLOOR AND LIMBER HOLE ASSEMBLY

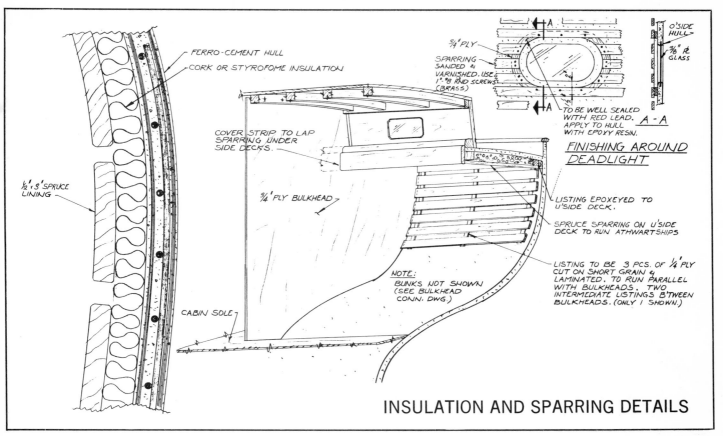

FERRO-CEMENT HULL
CORK OR STYROFOME INSULATION
½" x 3" SPRUCE LINING
CABIN SOLE

COVER STRIP TO LAP SPARRING UNDER SIDE DECKS.
¾" PLY BULKHEAD

NOTE:
BUNKS NOT SHOWN
(SEE BULKHEAD
CONN. DWG.)

¾" PLY
SPARRING SANDED & VARNISHED. USE 1"-8 RND SCREWS (BRASS)
O'SIDE HULL
⅜" R. GLASS
TO BE WELL SEALED WITH RED LEAD. APPLY TO HULL WITH EPOXY RESIN.
A - A

FINISHING AROUND DEADLIGHT

LISTING EPOXEYED TO U'SIDE DECK.
SPRUCE SPARRING ON U'SIDE DECK TO RUN ATHWARTSHIPS
LISTING TO BE 3 PCS. OF ¼" PLY CUT ON SHORT GRAIN & LAMINATED. TO RUN PARALLEL WITH BULKHEADS. TWO INTERMEDIATE LISTINGS B'TWEEN BULKHEADS. (ONLY 1 SHOWN.)

INSULATION AND SPARRING DETAILS

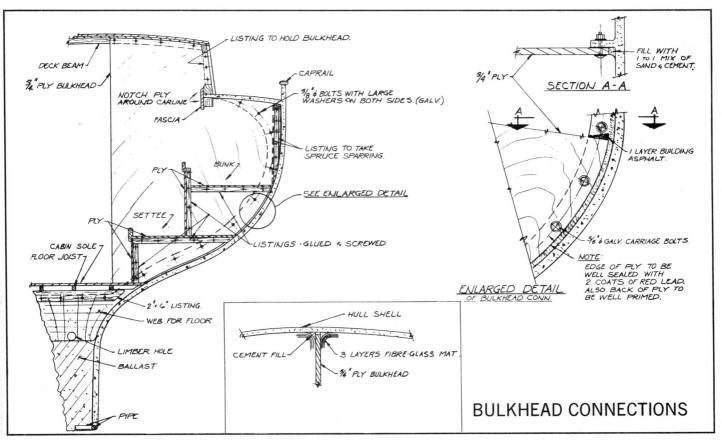

DECK BEAM
¾" PLY BULKHEAD
NOTCH PLY AROUND CARLINE
FASCIA
PLY
BUNK
PLY
SETTEE
CABIN SOLE
FLOOR JOIST
2"-6" LISTING.
WEB FOR FLOOR
LIMBER HOLE
BALLAST
PIPE

LISTING TO HOLD BULKHEAD.
CAPRAIL
⅜" ⌀ BOLTS WITH LARGE WASHERS ON BOTH SIDES. (GALV.)
LISTING TO TAKE SPRUCE SPARRING.

SEE ENLARGED DETAIL

LISTINGS - GLUED & SCREWED

FILL WITH 1 to 1 MIX OF SAND & CEMENT.
¾" PLY

SECTION A-A

1 LAYER BUILDING ASPHALT.
⅜" ⌀ GALV. CARRIAGE BOLTS.

NOTE:
EDGE OF PLY TO BE WELL SEALED WITH 2 COATS OF RED LEAD. ALSO BACK OF PLY TO BE WELL PRIMED.

ENLARGED DETAIL
OF BULKHEAD CONN.

HULL SHELL
CEMENT FILL
3 LAYERS FIBRE-GLASS MAT.
¾" PLY BULKHEAD

BULKHEAD CONNECTIONS

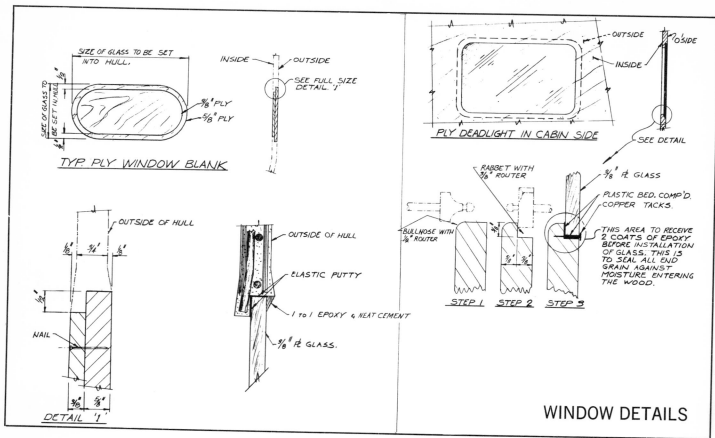

WINDOW DETAILS

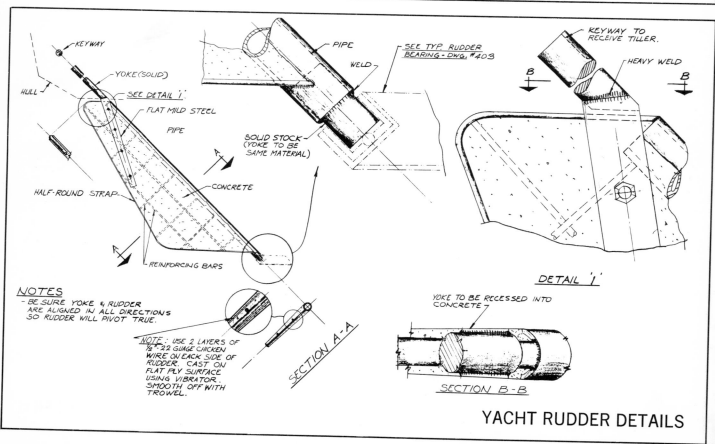

YACHT RUDDER DETAILS

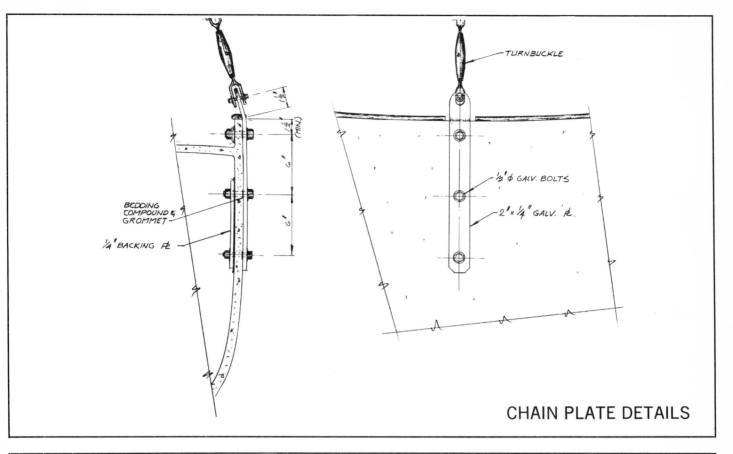

BEDDING
COMPOUND &
GROMMET

¼" BACKING ℞

TURNBUCKLE

½"ø GALV. BOLTS

2" x ¼" GALV. ℞.

CHAIN PLATE DETAILS

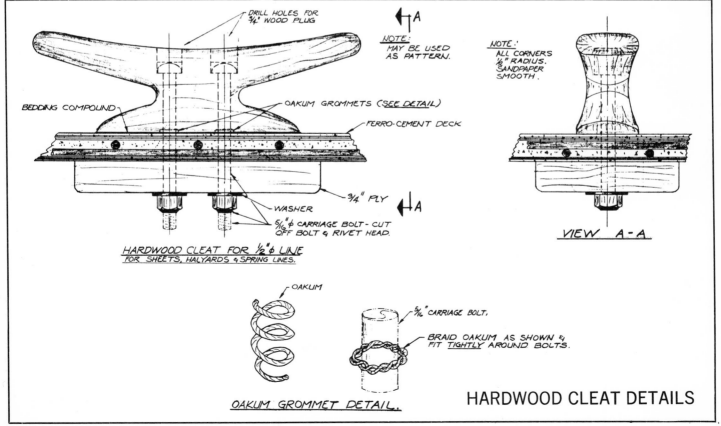

DRILL HOLES FOR
¾" WOOD PLUG

NOTE:
MAY BE USED
AS PATTERN.

NOTE:
ALL CORNERS
½" RADIUS.
SANDPAPER
SMOOTH.

BEDDING COMPOUND

OAKUM GROMMETS (SEE DETAIL)

FERRO-CEMENT DECK

¾" PLY

WASHER

5/16"ø CARRIAGE BOLT - CUT
OFF BOLT & RIVET HEAD.

VIEW A-A

HARDWOOD CLEAT FOR ½"ø LINE
FOR SHEETS, HALYARDS & SPRING LINES.

OAKUM

5/16" CARRIAGE BOLT.

BRAID OAKUM AS SHOWN &
FIT TIGHTLY AROUND BOLTS.

OAKUM GROMMET DETAIL.

HARDWOOD CLEAT DETAILS

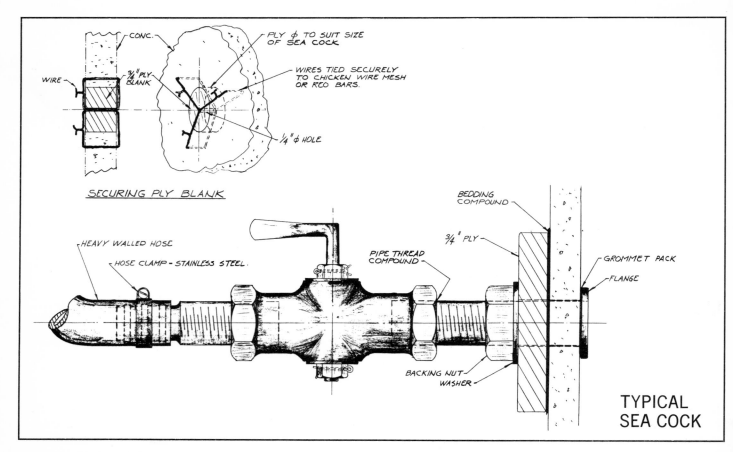

SECURING PLY BLANK

CONC.

WIRE

3/4" PLY
4" BLANK

PLY ∅ TO SUIT SIZE
OF SEA COCK

WIRES TIED SECURELY
TO CHICKEN WIRE MESH
OR REO BARS.

1/4" ∅ HOLE

HEAVY WALLED HOSE

HOSE CLAMP - STAINLESS STEEL.

PIPE THREAD
COMPOUND

BEDDING
COMPOUND

3/4" PLY

GROMMET PACK

FLANGE

BACKING NUT
WASHER

TYPICAL
SEA COCK

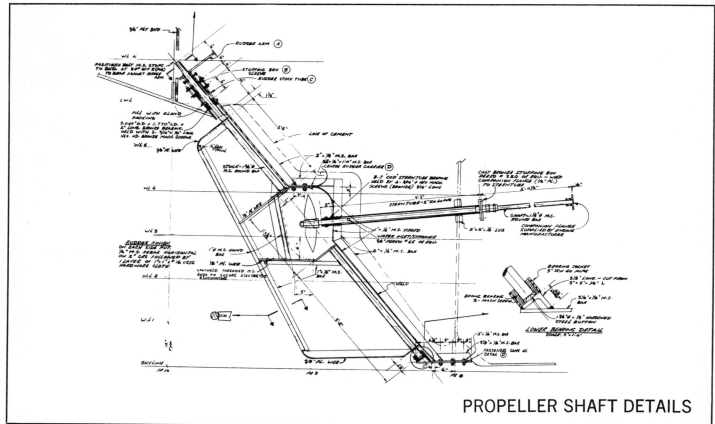

PROPELLER SHAFT DETAILS

CHAPTER 15

QUESTIONS AND ANSWERS

In the time that the Samson Marine Design Company has been in business, providing builders with plans and information on building in ferro-cement, it has been bombarded by a variety of questions.

A couple of dozen of the more common questions are reproduced here—together with the answers. These are the problems which seem to worry the would-be builder more than any others and the following answers will help give a clearer insight to the medium and get him away to a better start. Many of the points are of course covered in greater detail elsewhere in this book.

1. What exactly is ferro-cement?

Ferro-cement is the name given to a highly reinforced mortar. It is a dense mortar made up from common Portland cement, fine sand and pozzolan trowelled onto a framework of pipe, rod and chicken wire. This gives a thin but very strong slab with the chicken wire establishing a very fine distribution of reinforcement, with the rods supplying the main tensile strength.

2. What makes ferro-cement watertight?

Watertightness in ferro-cement is achieved simply by the density of the mortar mix. Density is reached by the use of very fine sand particles used in conjunc-

tion with the cement paste. The paste completely encloses the fine particles gluing them into a solid mass. Further density and strength is obviously achieved by the introduction into this mix of the rod and mesh framework. Serving a secondary purpose, the metals further prevent the mortar from cracking — a normal occurrence in the use of such a rich mixture.

3. How heavy is ferro-cement in comparison to other boat-building materials?

Ferro-cement is considered by designers as a reasonably heavy boat-building material. Actual weight is in the region of 10 lbs. per square foot at ¾-inch. A 40-foot hull of ferro-cement would probably average out heavier than a similar boat built in aluminum or fibreglass. It would also be heavier than a 40-foot light displacement wooden boat, but would equal the heavy displacement wooden or steel vessel.

4. How does ferro-cement stand up to impact?

Our conservative answer is "reasonably well". We do not claim it indestructible but at least it is an equal to any heavy displacement wooden hull. In fact, we have seen a ferro-cement hull hit a submerged reef at 10 knots and do no more damage than a light scoring of the keel. The hard-rock reef was not so fortunate—it was sheared off completely!

In general, collision impact will not produce any large cracks in ferro-cement. Rather, the impact will produce an egg-shell type of local damage preventing water entering the hull in large volume.

5. How does ferro-cement stand up to heavy seas?

Dr. Bob Griffiths of the 53-foot cutter "Awanhee" is the builder and owner of the first ferro-cement boat ever sailed around the world. He has made a winter passage of Cape Horn from East to West and a winter passage from Japan to Vancouver via the Aleutian Islands and Alaska. He reports that he encountered no troubles whatsoever with the construction.

6. How is ferro-cement cured?

After the ferro-cement mortar has been applied to the framework it must cure for a minimum of three weeks. This is achieved by keeping the hull continually wet, particularly if the humidity is low. If there is a lot of sun and wind, the hull should be covered with burlap and both the inside and outside of the skin should be kept wet. The hulls may also be steam cured.

7. Do you paint ferro-cement?

Briefly, yes. When the hull has cured and has been rubbed down with a carborundum stone, it should be etched with a diluted muriatic acid. When this is rinsed clear, two coats of epoxy resin are applied to seal in any stray ends of the mesh. Anti-fouling paint is applied to the bottom while the top-sides are coloured to suit.

8. What is the best kind of cement?

Type 5 Portland. This is slow setting and allows the amateur time to finish the job. This cement is also sulphate resistant—a corrosive element in sea-water. Most types of Portland cement will do.

9. What is the best kind of sand?

A sharp, clean, igneous sand which will completely pass a No. 8 sieve cannot be bettered. It should give a 15 percent passing of a No. 100 sieve with an even grading curve of sieve sizes in between. Sand is a very important part of ferro-cement and must be selected with care.

10. Should additives be used in ferro-cement construction?

This is a complex question and in general, the use of retarding agents is doubtful. The use of bonding agents may be considered if the cementing is to be done in stages. Pozzolan is always used as a densifier. Air entrainment agents may be used with caution.

11. What type of rod is best for construction?

A low carbon hard-drawn wire which has not been stress-relieved. Stressing steel as used in construction or cold rolled bar, depending on the construction method.

12. How are deck fittings attached?

Fittings are through-bolted to the deck. The cement is easily drilled with a carbide tip drill.

13. How do you attach hull fittings?

Through-hull fittings are blanked off prior to cementing or drilled later. The fittings are bedded with a plastic putty after an oakum grommett has been wrapped around the inside of the outside flange.

14. How do you attach dead lights?

These are again blanked out at the same time as other hull fittings.

15. How do you install the shaft log?

Complete installation details are given with the Samson Marine Design plans but briefly it is a stern tube imbedded in a strong shock-absorbing deadwood.

16. How about woodwork and joinery details?

Full details are included with the S.M.D.E. plans. Bulkheads are attached to special webs made up of ferro-cement during construction.

17. Can multi-hulls be built in ferro-cement?

No. Ferro-cement is too heavy for this type of construction.

18. How are ferro-cement boats insulated?

Adequate insulation can be achieved with cork or styrofoam bonded to the hull with any recommended adhesive.

19. Does condensation affect ferro-cement?

The ferro-cement boat is affected by condensation in the same way as any aluminum or fibreglass craft. It is, however, easily cured with proper insulation and ventilation.

20. How do you repair hull damage?

Repair technique is simple. The damaged area of mortar is pulverized, using a heavy weight on one side and hammer on the other. The area is cleaned of the cement particles and wire framework hammered back into shape. The area is then re-plastered and an epoxy or latex bonding-agent applied to the edges of the wound.

21. Is there anything to fear from electrolysis and galvanic action?

Apparently not. Ferro-cement acts as a natural insulator and no damage has been reported to date.

22. Is there any problem with engine vibration?

No. In Samson Marine Design plans, engine beds are designed to eliminate any damage from vibration. Most stationary engines are set on concrete pads.

23. Can fuel and water tanks be built-in?

Yes, these tanks can be cast in place if desired, but provision must be made for an inspection plate. It is wise to use a coat of epoxy on the inside of the tank.

24. Can you convert a wooden boat design to ferro-cement?

Yes and No, but in general we advise against it. To achieve a conversion successfully, the boat must be almost completely re-designed. To begin with, every boat is designed with the building material fully in mind. There are obviously great weight differences in the various building materials. For example, a fibreglass design should not be attempted in wood or steel. It is the same with ferro-cement. In the long-term view, the plans are only a small cost of the finished boat and wise spending in this area will give its reward in good performance. Stresses in boats react differently in the different mediums and must be taken into account. So again, only approach a conversion with the strictest caution and with fully qualified advice.

25. How about insurance?

Due to the fact that ferro-cement is fireproof, the boats are treated very favorably.

26. What is known about the physical properties of ferro-cement?

Very little scientific data has been gathered to date but the Canadian government is now leading the world in research in combination with industry to develop this excellent material for the ultimate benefit of the nations of the world.

27. How many ferro-cement boats are there around today?

A recent survey showed there were some 400 commercial and pleasure craft under construction and in the water.

After ten months in construction, this Samson Marine designed
36′ C-SHELL ketch was launched in Japan. Owner-builder Shigeo
Kitano invested less than $1000 in the boat to this stage.

CHAPTER 16

DESIGN SECTION

In the following pages you will see the many designs in sail, power and workboats which Samson Marine Design Enterprises Ltd. has drawn up specifically for ferro-cement construction. The builder no longer has to take a chance on a wooden boat plan conversion. New designs are continually being added to the S.M.D.E. list, keeping this pioneer company way out ahead in ferro-cement design and thinking, and offering the customer the most varied selection of plans on the market today. Only a selection of the company's range of stock designs are illustrated in this section. Many other designs are available. The company has a vast source of technical information on ferro-cement construction at its disposal, much of this drawn from hundreds of successful boats built to their design. With this information, backed by a team of highly qualified naval architects, marine engineers and boat-builders who have practical experience, the company undertakes a wide variety of commercial custom design work. It has commercial and pleasure boats being built to its design in all corners of the world. Each boat building package offered by S.M.D.E. is unique, giving the builder not only top quality construction drawings together with detail drawings of all fittings and fabrications but also offering back-up consultant service in all areas of construction. Further details on any of these designs or the commercial service can be obtained from the company at Box 98, Ladner, B.C., Canada.

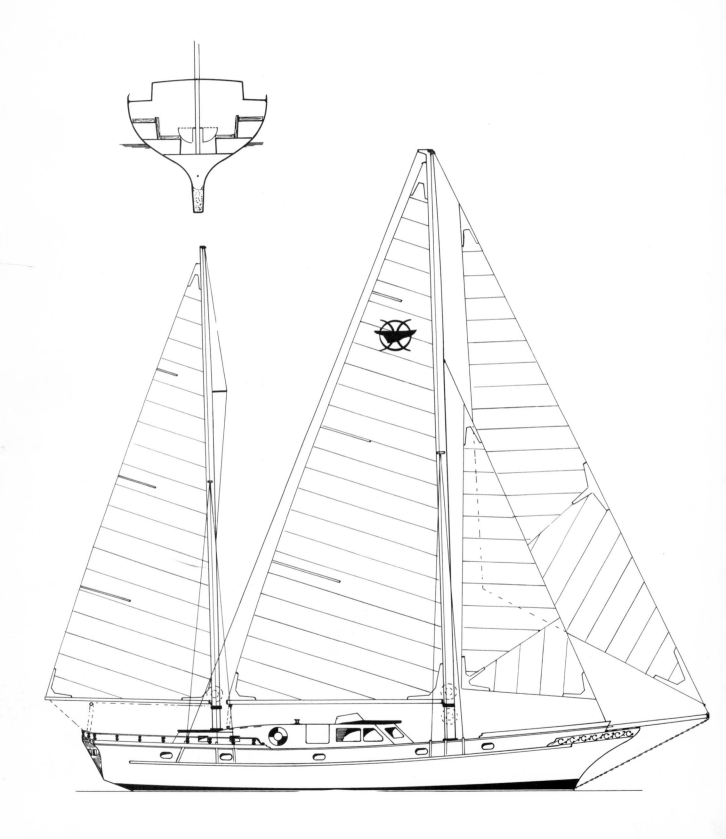

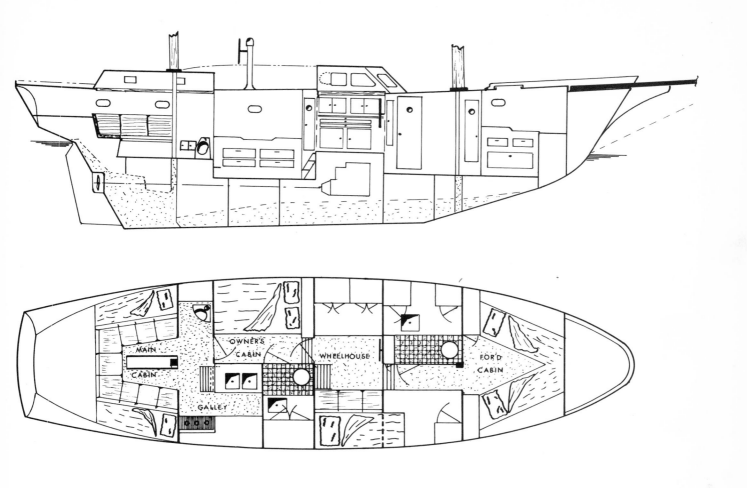

C-BREEZE
46 ft. Ketch

Length Overall: 45′ 6″	Auxiliary: 35 bhp diesel
Length Waterline: 38′ 4″	Sail Area: 1,050 sq. ft.
Beam: 13′	Headroom: 6′ 6″
Draft: 7′	Displacement: 20 tons

When Samson Marine Design first decided to offer plans for the home and professional builder, John Samson drew on his cruising experience to put together a boat which would meet almost every demand. The result was this 46′ ketch penned initially by naval architect Cecil Norris and completed by fellow naval architect Peter Noble.

The *C-Breeze* is the most popular design in the S.M.D.E. stock plan range.

The *C-Breeze* is a beautiful cruising or charter boat which cleverly combines traditional and modern stylings. She has been described as the near perfect boat for the man wanting to get away from it all and it is now an established fact that *C-Breeze* has turned that dream into a reality for many builders.

Perhaps her greatest attraction has been economy. Samson Marine Design confidently stand behind their statement that the home builder can produce the hull and deck of this boat for a materials cost of well under $2000. This represents a fantastic saving in a boat of this size and it is not unlikely that the boat could be finished at a cost of $10,000 to $15,000.

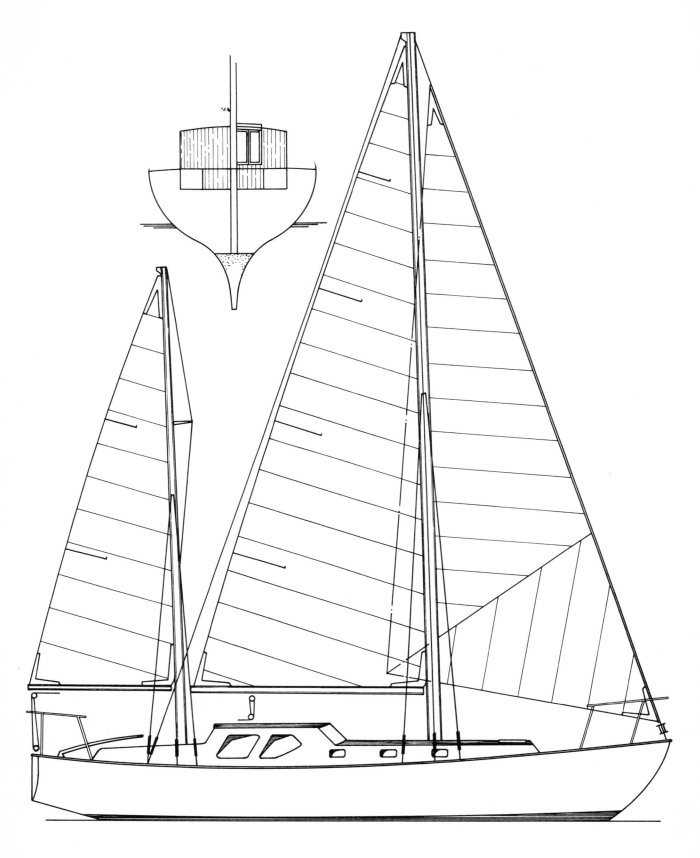

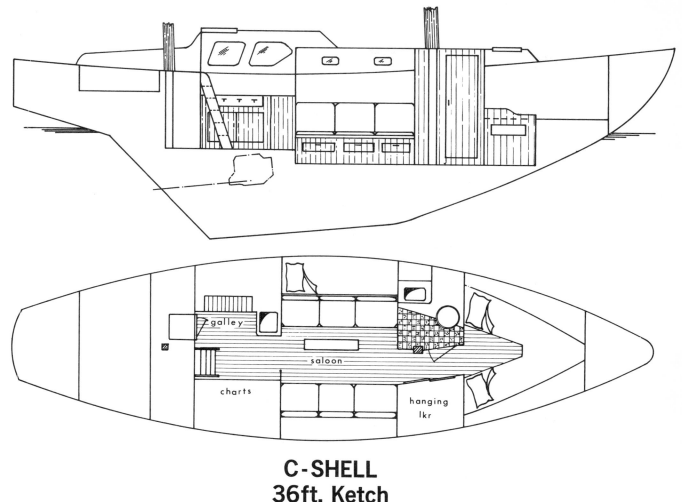

C-SHELL
36ft. Ketch

Length Overall: 36'
Length Waterline: 28' 4"
Draft: 6' 3"
Beam: 11'

Sail Area: 585 sq. ft.
Auxiliary: 10-15 bhp diesel
Headroom: 6' 2"

The 36' ocean going ketch *C-Shell* was the second stock design produced by S.M.D.E. She was again a John Samson brainchild—a boat designed to meet both the needs of the deep-sea cruising man and the weekender. More modest in concept than the *C-Breeze* and consequently a more economical proposition, she quickly proved equally popular with the ferro-cement boat builders.

One of the major features considered in this design was ease of construction by the amateur builder. This explains the plumb transom which makes her easy to set up initially while her main cabin and cockpit are one continuous cutout to simplify the addition of

a wooden superstructure. This is a feature of many of the stock designs which followed.

Again, the most attractive feature of the *C-Shell* design was her overall economy. Many builders have already proved the S.M.D.E. claim that the hull and decks could be put together for a material cost of under $1,000. Many builders are also proving that the boat can be completed for $6,000 to $7,000.

Ask any experienced cruising man what size of boat he prefers for his ocean travels and nine times out of ten the answer will be "Around 36 feet". Ask him what features he would like in that boat and you will probably find them all incorporated in *C-Shell*.

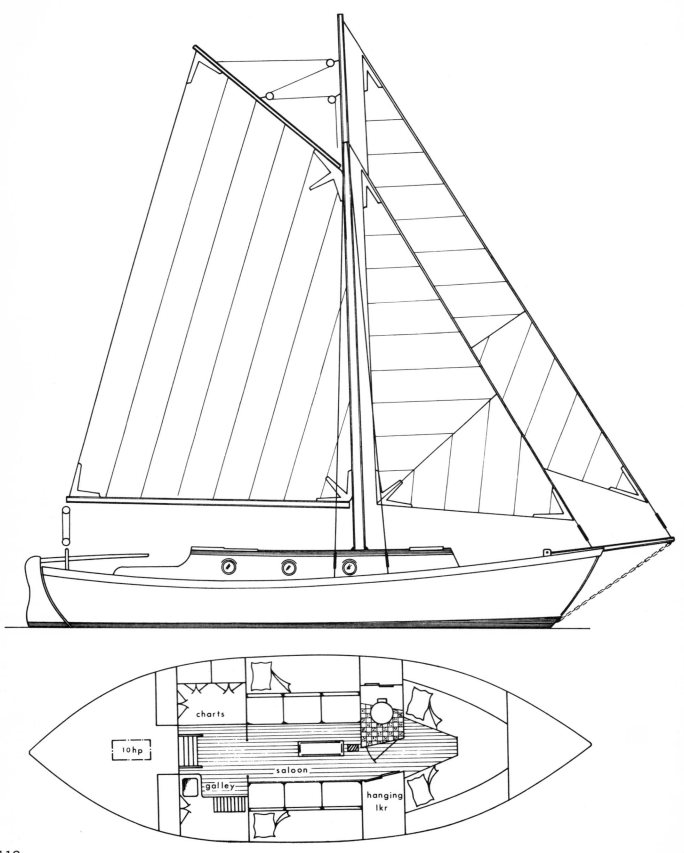

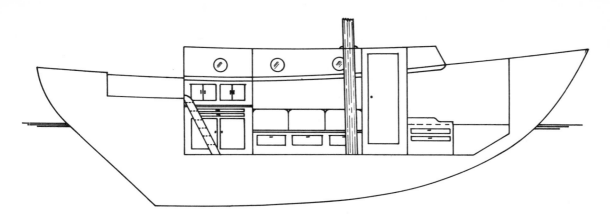

C-MIST
32 ft. Double-Ended Gaff Cutter

Length Overall: 32' 2"   Auxiliary: 10 hp
Length Waterline: 27' 6"   Berths: 6
Beam: 11' 2"   Headroom: 6' 2"
Draft: 5'   Water Cap.: 75 gals.
Displacement: 18,750 lbs. Fuel Cap.: 20 gals.
             Sail Area: 605 sq. ft.

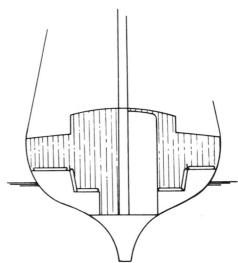

Tradition has always played an important role in boat design and the following three sailboats clearly emphasize this fact.

The little gaff-rigged cutter *C-Mist* is the type of boat to appeal to the most demanding traditionalist—and not only because of her sail-rig. She is double-ended and beamy with lines that can only be described as salty. Naval architects Peter Noble and Ken Davies designed *C-Mist* for themselves. They built the hull in about 350 hours at a cost of approximately $750. *C-Mist* is the smallest sailboat in the Samson Marine range and certainly the easiest to build.

The larger 39' ketch *C-Farer* displays very traditional lines. In fact, she would probably be described by nine out of every ten sailers as a "typical Tahiti ketch". The design was penned by Ken Davies and met a healthy demand from boat-builders who wanted tradition tied with the exciting ferro-cement medium.

Last, but by no means least, is the majestic 53' schooner *C-Lord*.

Long before the plan drawings were completed for this design, an eager boat building market was clamoring for a glimpse at her lines. The builders were certainly not disappointed with *C-Lord's* eye appeal and the first boat was under construction before its last blueprint was completed.

It is fitting that this first *C-Lord*, being built commercially, will go into service as a charter boat among the beautiful Gulf Islands of British Columbia — her native home.

It is likely that before long her sister ships will dot every corner of the globe—many of these under charter licence—a duty for which she is ideally suited.

With this design, Scottish-born naval architect Peter Noble has shown most clearly the versatility of the ferro-cement medium. Nothing is too big nor too small—no shape too difficult. The charm of a bygone era is recaptured and complimented by a modern day technique.

C-FARER
39 ft. Double-Ended Ketch

Length Overall: 38′ 6″
Length Waterline: 33′ 4″
Beam: 10′ 9″
Draft: 5′ 6″
Displacement: 26,800 lbs.

Sail Area: 840 sq. ft.
Auxiliary: 20 hp
Berths: 4-5
Headroom: 6′ 3″
Water Cap.: 70 gals.

Fuel Cap.: 25 gals.

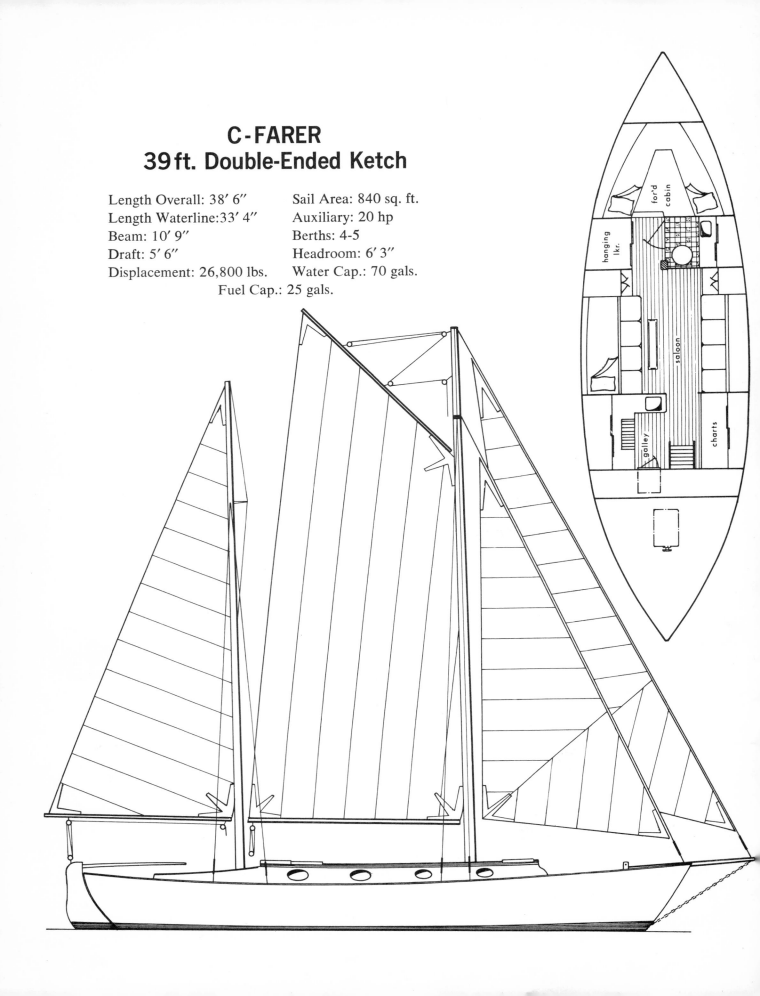

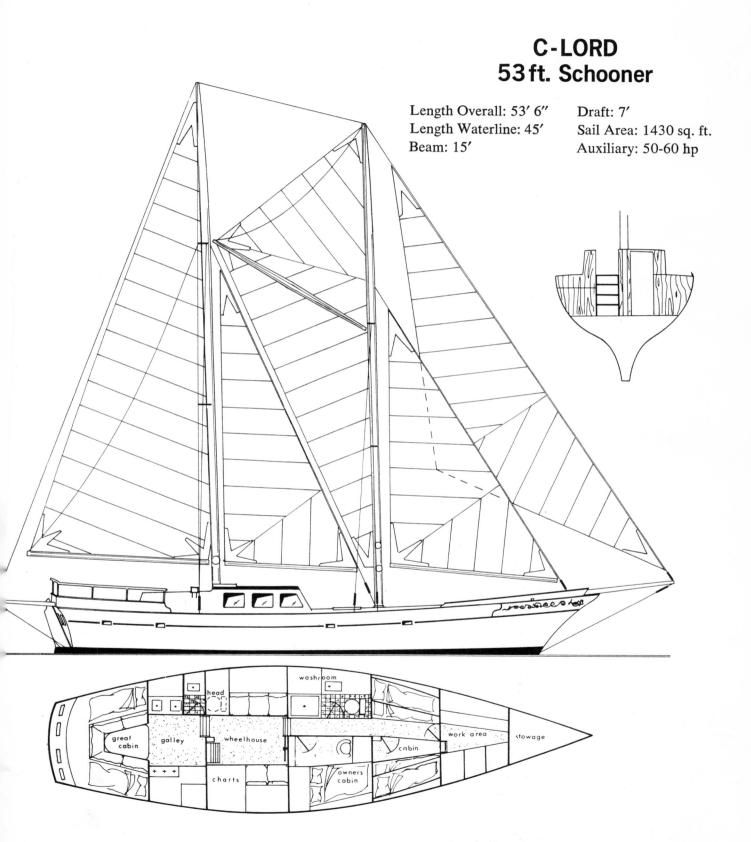

C-LORD
53 ft. Schooner

Length Overall: 53' 6"   Draft: 7'
Length Waterline: 45'   Sail Area: 1430 sq. ft.
Beam: 15'   Auxiliary: 50-60 hp

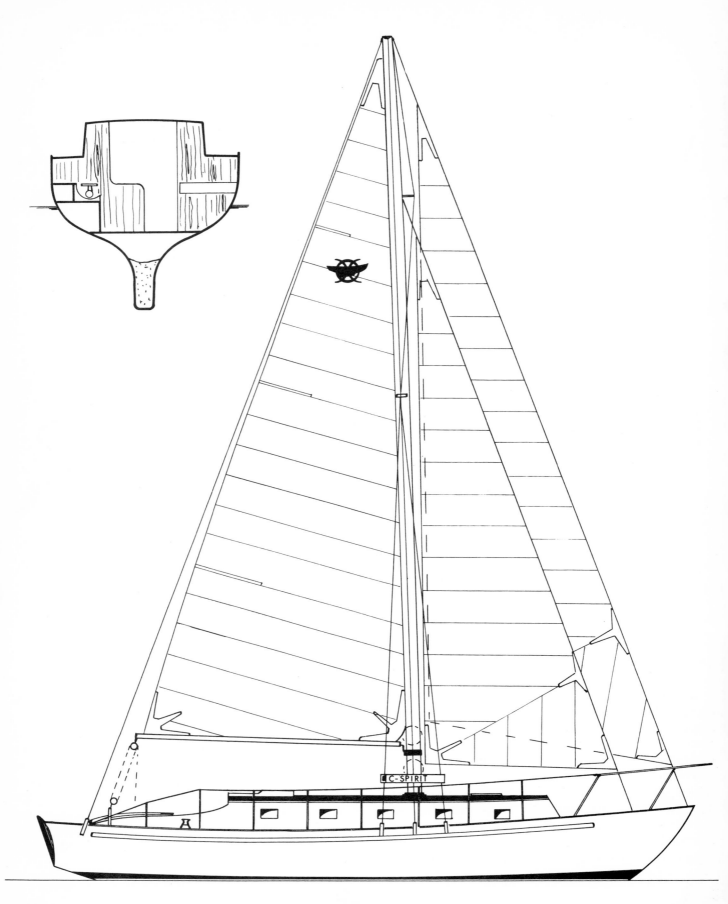

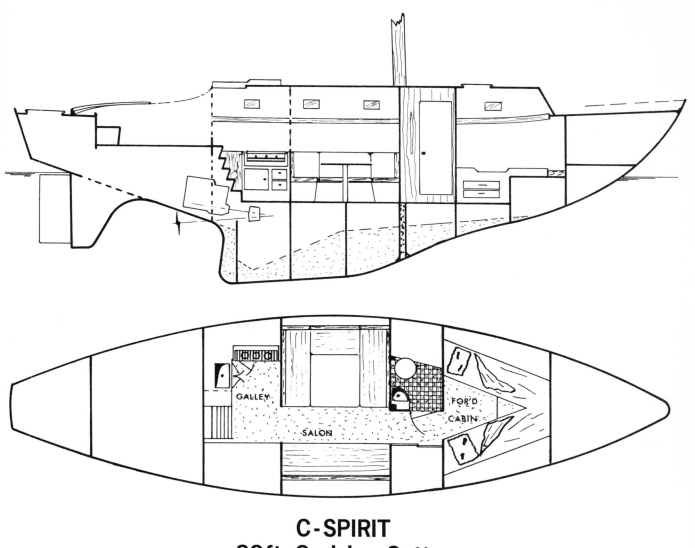

C-SPIRIT
39ft. Cruising Cutter

Length Overall: 39′ 2″	Draft: 6′ 8″
Length Waterline: 32′ 2″	Sail area: 800
Beam: 11′ 2″	Auxiliary: 35 bhp diesel

It was John Samson again who inspired the design of the 39′ cruising cutter *C-Spirit*. It was always his contention that a boat could be designed in ferro-cement to complete a reasonably fast circumnavigation. Actually, Samson, John Simpson and Cecil Norris put their heads together over the design. They settled on the masthead cutter rig for efficiency, an aft skeg for maneuverability, deep draft for seaworthiness and ample accommodation for privacy and extended living on board.

In many ways *C-Spirit* reflects a breakthrough in ferro-cement design moving away from the long deep keel conception.

C-Spirit does of course retain ample draft, supporting John Samson's contention that in his extensive ocean cruising experience he has never found this to be a hindrance. He reflects he is happier to have a lot of boat underneath him when the wind pipes up.

In common with all the sail boat designs in the Samson Marine stock range, provision is made for furling gears and roller reefing and many other sailing aids.

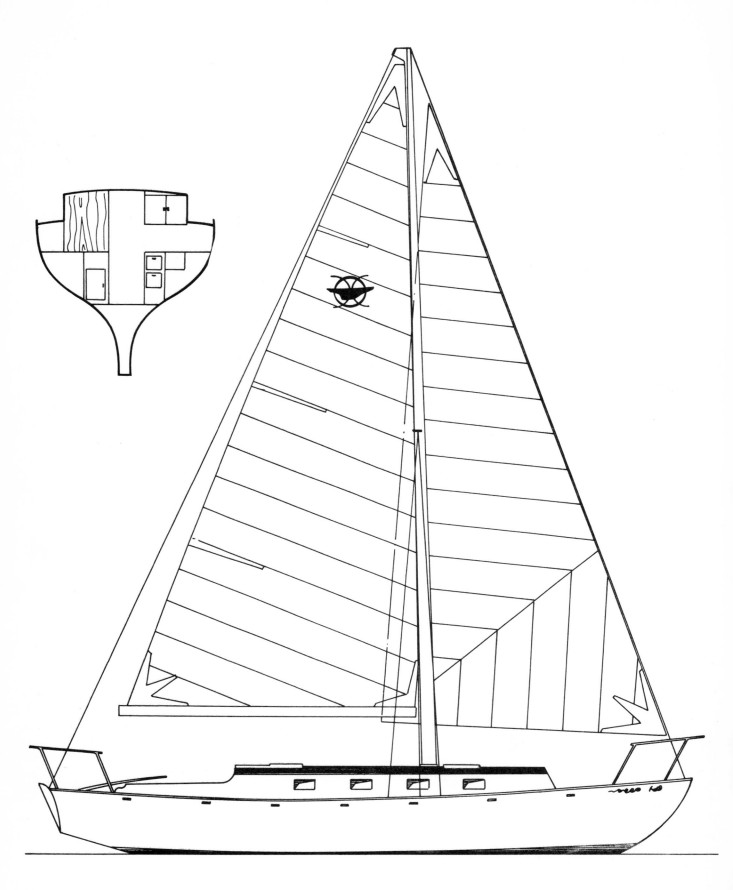

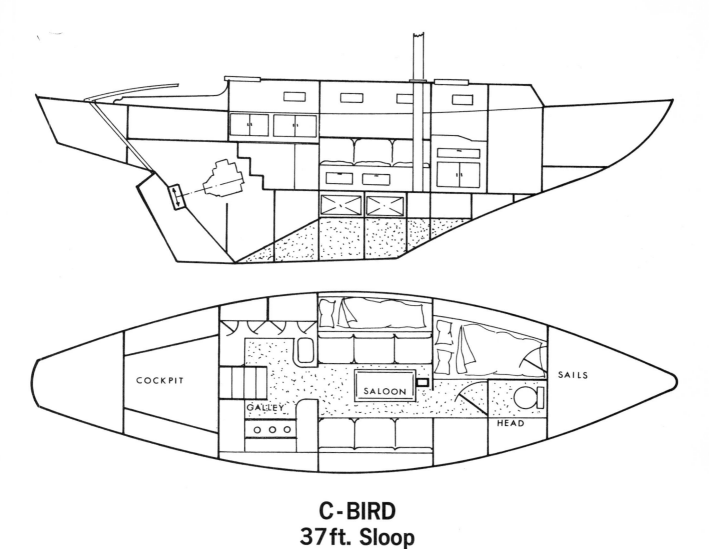

C-BIRD
37 ft. Sloop

Length Overall: 37′ 5″   Sail Area: 620 sq. ft.
Length Waterline: 28′ 4″   Auxiliary: 20 bhp diesel
Beam: 10′ 9″   Headroom: 6′ 2″
Draft: 6′   Displacement: 20,200 lbs.

One of the most frequent requests by early builders in ferro-cement was for a sloop rigged boat like *C-Shell*. That explains how Samson Marine came to the creation of their 37′ sloop *C-Bird*. Obviously there was little point in producing *C-Shell* with just a sloop rig — a complete new design was the answer and the result is a 37-footer which is probably the fastest hull in the stock plan range. Of course, the priority was a boat which would fully qualify as a blue water sailer.

Designer Peter Noble made minor changes in the original lines of the *C-Shell* to give a slimmer underwater section and at the same time increased the overall length by raking the transom. The accommodation was also modified and to present a different profile the dog house was removed. It is still possible to interchange accommodations with the *C-Bird* and *C-Shell* if preferred. This is a feature which many builders have taken advantage of.

The economy tag applies equally to the *C-Bird* with her construction costs almost identical to those of the *C-Shell*.

C-SPRAY
34ft. Centreboard Sloop

Length Overall: 34'
Length Waterline: 27' 6"
Beam: 11' 6"
Draft: 3' 9"

Sail Area: 630 sq. ft.
Auxiliary: 10-15 bhp diesel
Headroom: 6'
Displacement: 17,800 lbs.

The 34' centreboard sloop *C-Spray* was the next design tackled by S.M.D.E. She was created to meet the demand from the shallow draft sailers in the type of shoal waters encountered around the Caribbean.

Representing the traditional, *C-Spray* has been described as a perfect substitute for the weekend cottage. Designer Peter Noble sees her as a boat willing to go anywhere and easy to handle. The fact that she could be completed for under $6,000 puts her within the range of any fun-seeking family—providing that the family is willing to put a little effort into her construction.

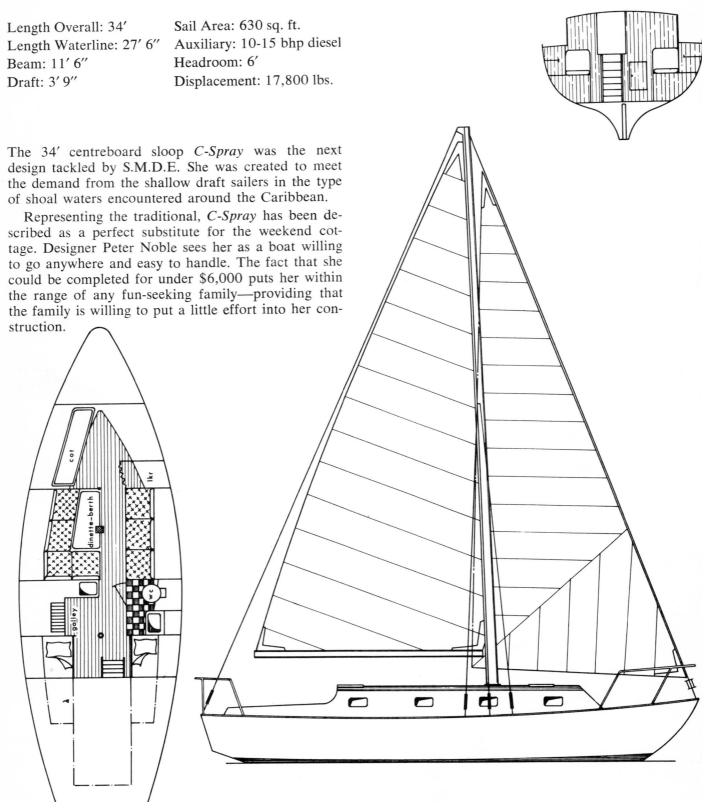

C-ROVER
44ft. Power Cruiser

Length Overall: 44'
Length Waterline: 40'
Beam: 13' 6''
Draft: 5' 3''
Displacement: 20.8 tons

Power: 150 shp
Speed: 10 knots
Range: 1300 nautical miles
Fuel Cap.: 1000 gal.
Water Cap.: 400 gal.

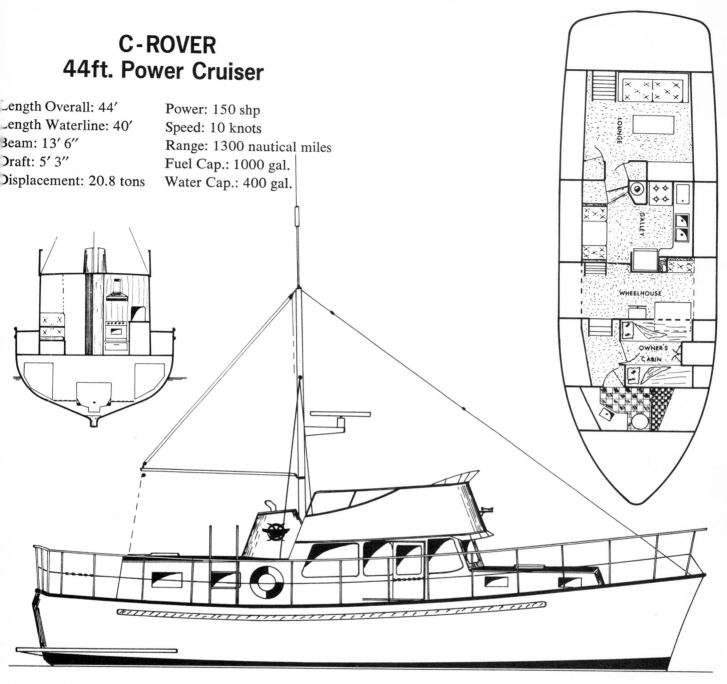

The versatility of the ferro-cement medium is underlined in the design of the 44' power cruiser *C-Rover*.

It seems that the sailing man, whether his bent be stick-and-canvas or smoke-and-fuel, constantly seeks something bigger and better. Samson Marine was asked to produce a design in the Grand Banks style for the big power boat enthusiast and John Simpson came up with one of the most striking designs in their range. Originally he designed *C-Rover* to meet the requirements of a Californian yachtsman, providing ideal accommodation for two people. This he later modified to give accommodation for at least six and turning the *C-Rover* into a dream home afloat for anyone.

It is perhaps interesting to look at the power requirements of such a vessel and a suggested power plant for the *C-Rover* is an engine which will deliver 150 shaft hp at 2600 rpm. This will push this boat along at a handy 10 knots and give her a cruising range of 1300 nautical miles.

This type of boat is ideally suited for construction in the web framework technique discussed in an earlier part of the book.

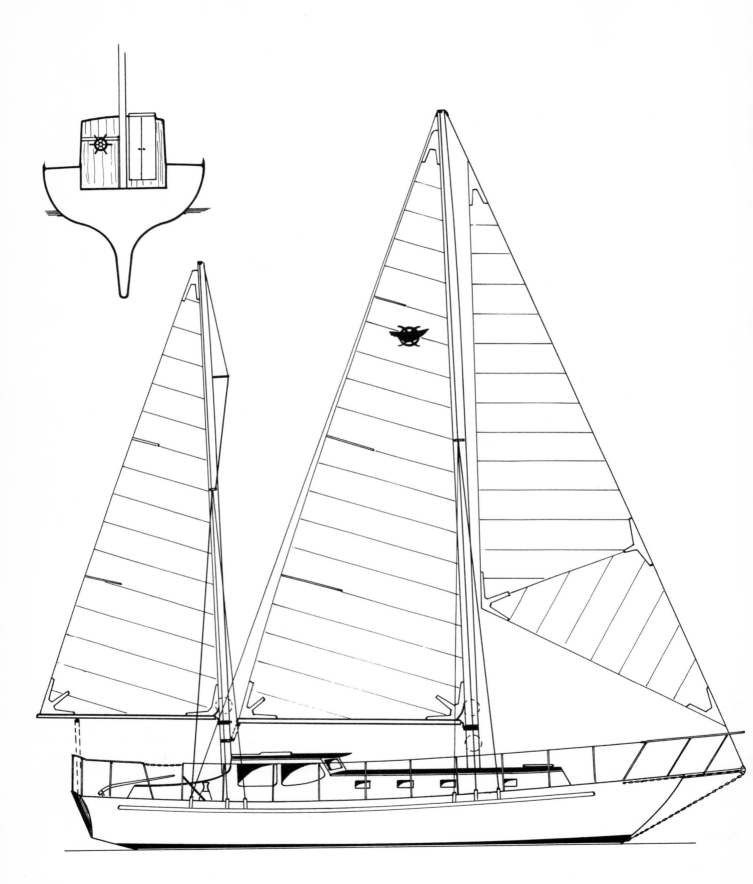

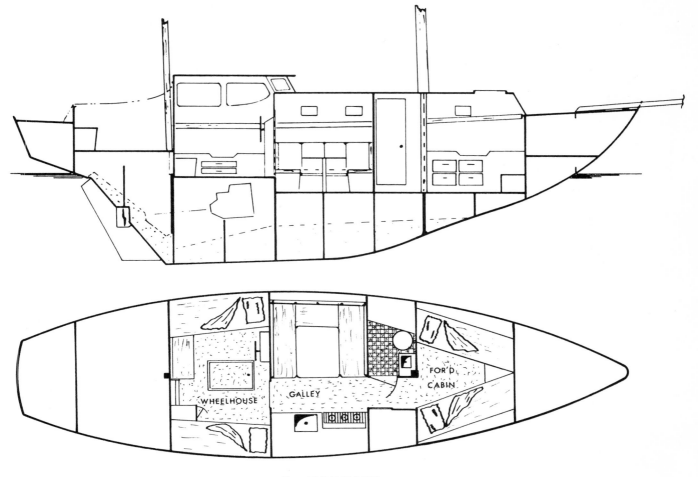

C-SMOKE
40 ft. Ketch

Length Overall: 40'   Auxiliary: 20 bhp diesel
Length Waterline: 31' 8"   Freeboard: 3'
Beam: 11' 5"   Displacement: 12 tons
Draft: 6'   Sail area: 720 sq. ft.

Headroom: 6' 3"

Back with the sail boat enthusiasts, Samson Marine were next requested to produce a "fill-in" design — a ketch of some 40' overall falling between the *C-Shell* and *C-Breeze* designs. Young Canadian designer John Simpson tackled the problem and the beautiful 40' *C-Smoke* was his answer.

Adaptability is the feature of this design. Although not illustrated here this six-berth blue water sailer can be outfitted with a small trunk cabin aft which houses two berths for children. This makes the design ideal in size and layout for a cruising family. The *C-Smoke* carries some 720 sq. ft. of sail which can be handled with ease by a crew of two. Below decks the accommodation plan shows luxury living for the family with a large galley and dinette area.

The home builder should expect to invest a little over $1000 in the construction of the hull and decks of this sun seeker.

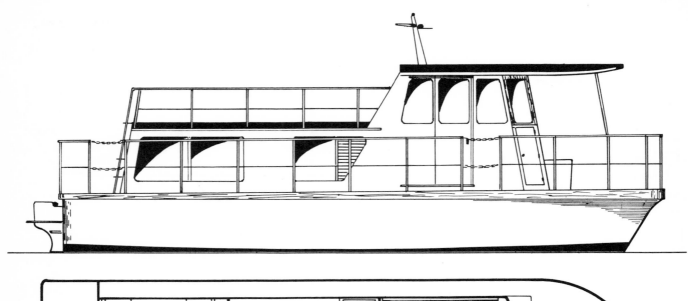

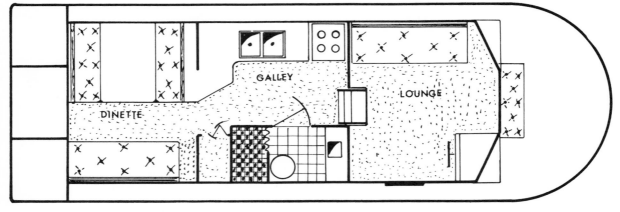

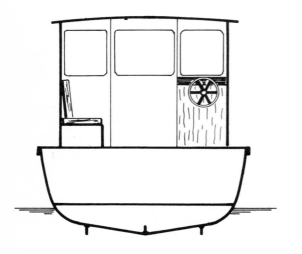

C-NOOK
32 ft. Houseboat

Length Overall: 32' 6"   Power: 2-20 hp outboard
Length Waterline: 30'   motors; or 1-40 hp
Beam: 11' 6"   Freeboard Aft: 3' 3"
Draft: 1' 6"   Freeboard Fwd: 3' 6"

Sleeping Accommodation: 6

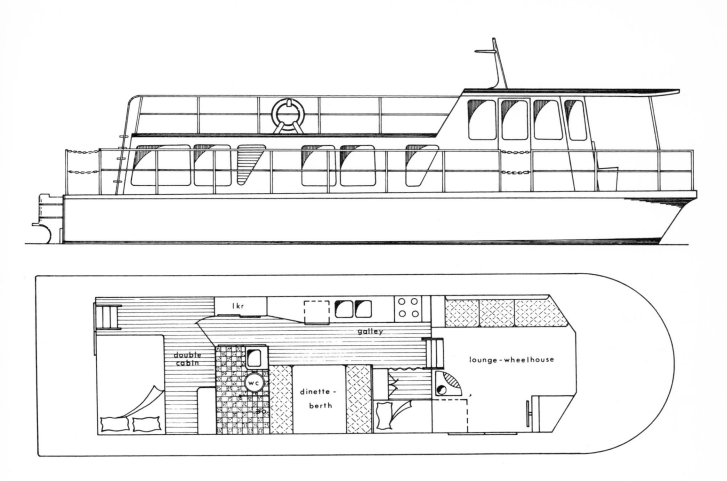

C-DRIFTER
40 ft. Houseboat

Length Overall: 40' 6"		Freeboard: 3' 3"	
Length Waterline: 38'		Displacement: 21,900 lbs.	
Beam: 12' 6"		Speed: 8 knots	
Draft: 1' 6"		Power: 2-30 hp outboards	

One of the fastest developing trends in pleasure boating is houseboating. It was natural that the fast developing ferro-cement interest should merge with the houseboat boom for mutual benefit.

The link was provided by two designs from the drawing board of John Simpson—the 32' *C-Nook* and the 40' *C-Drifter*.

The designs reflect up-to-date thinking in accommodation and styling together with all the advantages of the ferro-cement medium. Lack of maintenance heads the list in this regard — a prime requisite for the type of boat which is liable to sit idle in the water for a long period.

The Samson Marine houseboats have conventional hull form rather than pontoon fabrication, but it should be clearly understood that this type of vessel will only perform at its best in protected waters. It is not to be used in the open sea where the going can get rough.

Construction of this type of houseboat hull in ferro-cement is simple and inexpensive and moderate power is needed to achieve comfortable cruising speeds.

C-HORSE
38ft. Salmon Troller

Length Overall: 37′ 6″
Beam: 10′ 10″
Depth MLD: 6′ 3″
Draft Operating: 5′ 9″

Fuel Capacity: 510 gals.
Fresh Water: 250 gals.
Hold Capacity: 460 c.f.
Power: 60-80 bhp diesel

It was obvious that only one field of challenge remained for the pioneer design company after the earlier plans were completed, and that was the commercial field. For assistance in this area Samson Marine went to the veteran designer of fishing vessels, Bill Reid. Samson Marine supplied the facts on ferro-cement construction and Bill was able to fill the requirements of the fisherman. His 38′ West Coast Salmon Troller *C-Horse* reflects the adaption of his knowledge and experience to the ferro-cement medium.

The advantages of a ferro-cement working boat had quickly been realised — low maintenance, rot proof, insulated fish holds allowing ice to be kept on board longer; integral tanks and fish holds; easy to repair; numerous advantages putting more dollars in the fisherman's pocket.

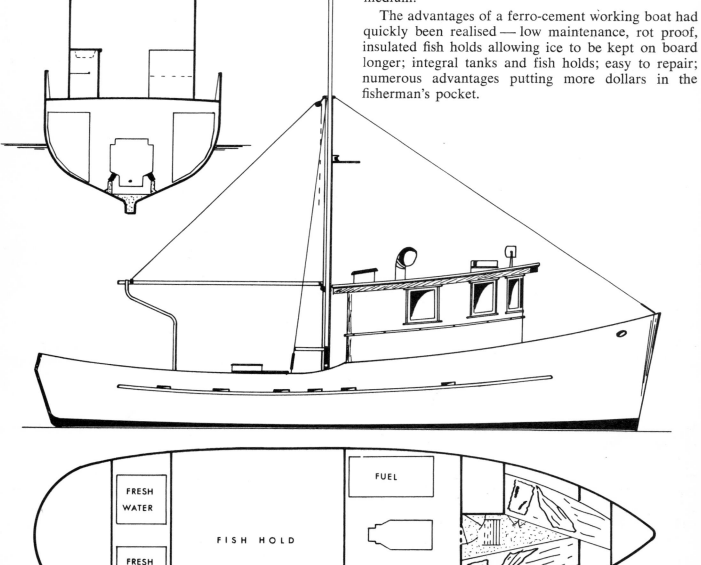

FRESH WATER

FRESH WATER

FISH HOLD

FUEL

FUEL

C-HARVESTER
44ft. Salmon Troller

Length Overall: 43′ 6½″   Fresh Water: 300 imp. gals.
Depth: 6′ 11¼″   Power: Cat D.330
Beam: 12′ 0″   135 h.p. at 2000 rpm
Hold Capacity: 580 cu. ft.   Fuel: 880 imp. gals.

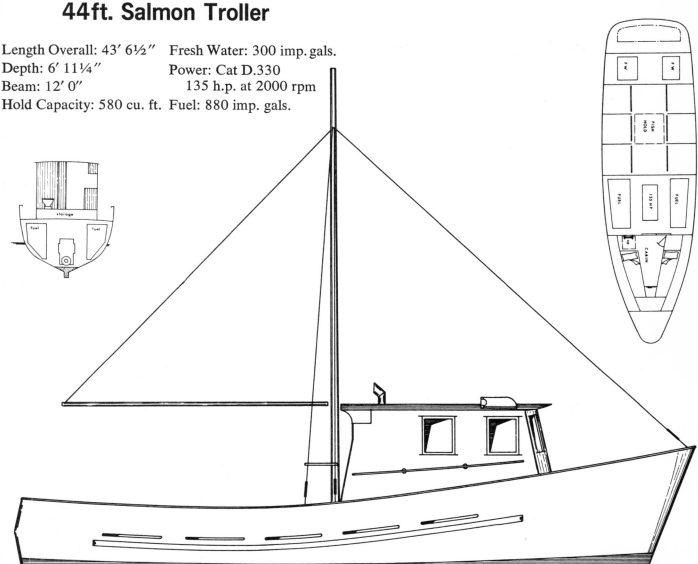

While the 38′ troller *C-Horse* quickly filled the need of many fishermen, many sought a vessel with a larger carrying capacity. This time designer Peter Noble drew on his experience in the fishing boat field and penned the 44′ *C-Harvester*. Adaptability is the highlight of this design, the vessel boasting the type of hull which can readily be employed in various methods of fishing.

The *C-Harvester* is a sturdy work boat of the type common on the west coast of North America and boasts a hold capacity of some 500 cubic feet of space. The mere size of this hold allows ease of engine installation through the portable plate dividing it from the engine area.

This design was immediately popular with the U.S. fishermen who ply their trade in Alaskan waters and to meet their specific needs Noble also produced a beamier version of the *C-Harvester* complete with live tanks, etc. This design, the *C-Gleaner,* is reproduced on Page 135.

It goes without saying that the front entry and easy forward sections of both the *C-Harvester* and *C-Gleaner* go to make very comfortable sea boats.

C-FISHER
53 ft. Workboat

Length Overall: 53' 9"
Beam: 16'
Depth: 7' 3"
Fish Hold Capacity:
   1000 cu. ft.

Fuel Oil: 1500 gals.
Fresh Water: 200 gals.
Engine: 150-250 hp
Crew: 4

A steady demand for a workboat design in the 50' to 60' range resulted in the *C-Fisher*. This was produced to meet the demand of various fisheries throughout the world. She was, in fact, commissioned for prawn trawling in Australia but is equally adaptable for bottom trawling, purse or drum seining and other specialized fishing.

As one example, king crab fishermen are finding their ferro-cement hold forms a tank for keeping the catch under circulating salt water.

The *C-Fisher* is the largest workboat design yet produced for the ferro-cement medium, but designers are already looking ahead to vessels of 70 to 100 feet overall.

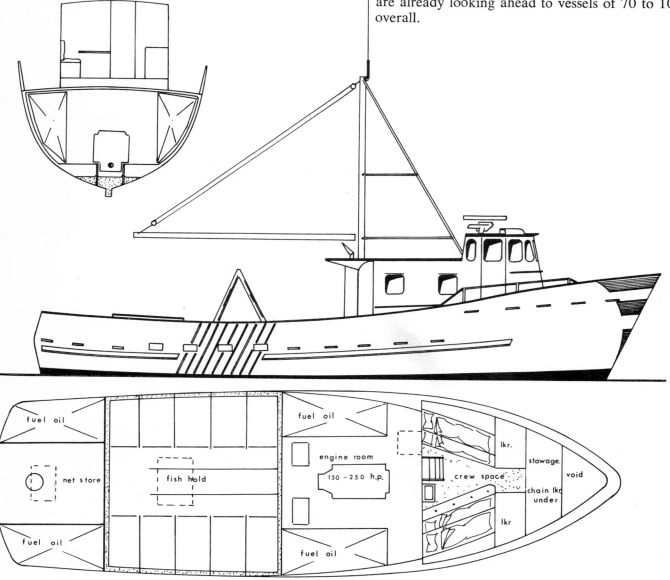

C-GLEANER
43ft. Combination Fishboat

Length Overall: 43′ 6″
Draft: 6′ 11″
Fuel Oil: 1160 gal.
Engine: 180-250 h.p.

Beam: 14′ 6″
Fish Hold Cap.: 600 cu. ft.
Fresh Water: 150 gal.
Fishing: Trawler/
Crab Boat

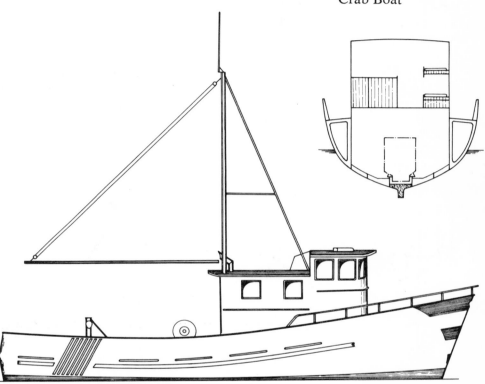

The demands and requirements of fishermen vary throughout the world and it was no surprise to Samson Marine when a particular group looked at the *C-Harvester* and said; "That is almost the boat we want — but not quite".

The fishermen were from Alaska and they were seeking a boat for crab and shrimp fishing. Their specific need was a beamier boat which would give them the necessary stability for live tanks.

Designer Peter Noble quickly came up with the answer — an adaptation of his *C-Harvester* design, the *C-Gleaner,* which can be used for crab and shrimp fishing as well as albacore and salmon trolling.

In this design, the beam is increased to 14 feet 6 inches and a hold capacity of 600 cu. ft. is gained. A raised pilot house gives the helmsman excellent

visibility and a flying bridge can be fitted if required.

Fish and fresh water tanks are built in ferro-cement for ease of construction and are fitted with large inspection hatches.

The *C-Gleaner* was designed for construction in the web framework technique — the latest building method developed by Samson Marine. The hull has frames spaced on two-foot centres making her both rugged and capable of withstanding a lot of hard use.

The *C-Gleaner* is ideally powered by a Cummins NH 250M which develops 180 horsepower at 1800 rpm. She will attain a speed of 9.5 knots when fully loaded.

IF AT FIRST YOU DON'T SUCCEED
That seems to be the motto of Jack Whitener of Niceville, Florida. Without any technical information at his disposal Jack went ahead and built himself this 16-foot flattie. As Jack himself says, "I only wish this book had been available at the time." But, if nothing else, Jack Whitener proved the medium and he is now moving on to bigger and better things.

ACKNOWLEDGEMENTS: The co-authors wish to acknowledge the following people for their help and co-operation in the compilation of this book. The development of the ferro-cement boat building technique has always been a co-operative effort and without a regular interchange of information and ideas, this book would never have been possible. To the following we are indebted: John Seeger and Floyd Swenson (Portland Cement Association, Vancouver), John Miller (Ocean Cement Company, Vancouver), Roger Johnson (Tree Island Steel Company, Vancouver), Mike Abbot, Ron Hook, Dick Simpson, Hal Burfitt, Shigeo Kitano, Bernie Skinner, Brian Walden, Scotty Jenkins, Keith Bassett, Jim Farrelly, Jeff Entrican, Syd Hewetson, C. H. Andrews, D. Barwell, Chas. Strange, Ron Carter, Dr. Bob Griffith, Brian Sinnott, Richard Hartley, D. Ryan, F. Bedford, The Vancouver Daily Province, Sea Spray Magazine (New Zealand), Julius Herman, Gordon Ellis, Ernie Watchorn, Jack Wagner, Reg Clarke, Hank Dirkson, Jim Kreeft, Hank Vandenburg, Art Kelly (B.C. Research Council), Rowland Morgan (University of Bristol), N. B. Hutcheon and J. H. Jenkins (Canadian Building Digest), C. F. Norris, W. Reid, I. Ross, A. Kruger, J. Simpson, E. Nybeck, T. Lee, M. Smith, The Portland Cement Association and the American Iron and Steel Institute.